THE HERON

A NEW NATURALIST SPECIAL VOLUME

The aim of THE NEW NATURALIST series is to interest the general reader in the wild life of Britain by recapturing the inquiring spirit of the old naturalists. The Editors believe that the natural pride of the British public in their native fauna and flora, to which must be added concern for their conservation, is best fostered by maintaining a high standard of accuracy combined with clarity of exposition in presenting the results of modern scientific research. The volumes in the main series deal with large groups of animals and plants, with the natural history of particular areas of habitats in Britain, and with certain special subjects. THE NEW NATURALIST SPECIAL VOLUMES, on the other hand, cover, in greater detail, a single species or group of species. In both the main series and specials the animals and plants are described in relation to their homes and habitats, and are portrayed in their full beauty with the help of both colour and monochrome photographs.

EDITORS:

JAMES FISHER M.A.

JOHN GILMOUR M.A.

JULIAN HUXLEY M.A. D.Sc. F.R.S.

L. DUDLEY STAMP C.B.E. D.Lit. D.Sc.

PHOTOGRAPHIC EDITOR:

ERIC HOSKING F.R.P.S.

Eric Hosking

Portrait of a heron nesting at Walthamstow (London Metropolitan Water Board)
Reservoir, May 1951

THE NEW NATURALIST

THE HERON

by

FRANK A. LOWE

With a Colour Frontispiece
15 Black and White Photographs
13 Drawings & Maps

COLLINS
ST. JAMES'S PLACE, LONDON
1954

TO BETTY

who for twenty-five years has shared

my birding

Printed in Great Britain by
Willmer Brothers & Co. Ltd., Birkenhead
for Collins Clear-Type Press, London and Glasgow

CONTENTS

LIST OF PLATES

MAPS AND DRAWINGS

EDITORS' PREFACE

WHEN THE EDITORIAL BOARD of the *New Naturalist* asked the author of *The Heron* about the circumstances in which his book came to be written, he replied rather typically "I find it easier to write about herons than about Frank A. Lowe".

Readers of *The Heron* will come to appreciate the author's modesty, while at the same time noticing that he has few reasons for it. This well-written, well-informed account of one of Britain's most famous and familiar large birds has been a labour of love for Frank Lowe for a long time. His delight and interest in his bird has led him to make long observations, and take fine photographs, of a local heron population and its heronry for many consecutive years. His substantial original contributions to our knowledge of heron behaviour, combined with a careful analysis of the world literature and marking-returns of the species, have given us the most valuable treatise on and summary of the life of the grey heron of the Old World (*Ardea cinerea*) yet published.

Frank Lowe, like most contributors to the *New Naturalist* series, can take pride in his amateur status. Like many amateur naturalists, he enjoys local natural history most particularly ; and many bird-watchers in the North of England must know him as a past President of the Lancashire and Cheshire Fauna Committee and of the Bolton Field Naturalists' Society, or as Chairman of the bird section of the North-West Naturalists' Union. Lowe earns his living in his family's business of manufacturing chemists, and spends much time every winter lecturing, particularly to schools, on natural history subjects : other valuable educational activities of his include a weekly column in the *Bolton Evening News* which he has written for nearly thirty years. It is nearly twenty years since he wrote a book ; an interval which his readers will agree with us has been far too long.

AUTHOR'S PREFACE

A WEALTH of heron lore is to be found in works in many languages. In a search of every source of information, I have sorely tried the patience of many of my friends. I have included in the bibliography those works which have been most interesting to me, but it is by no means complete. With very few exceptions I have consulted every work listed and the inclusion of a reference is also my acknowledgment to the author.

W. B. Alexander, custodian of the ornithological library in Oxford which bears his name, and G. B. Stratton, librarian to the Zoological Society of London, have been generous with both books and advice. My friends A. W. Boyd and the late Sir Hugh Gladstone have also lent me books from their libraries. I am specially grateful to Fr. Hausmann for his invaluable translations of German works.

My quest for information has often extended beyond even the most comprehensive of libraries and I am vastly indebted to many ornithologists for their letters and opinions, invariably given with great kindness and generosity. J. A. G. Barnes sent me an unpublished account of a fatal territorial combat between herons. Jacques Berlioz gave me facts on the status of the heron in France. Dr. M. F. Mörzer Bruijns provided me with a copy, before publication, of the results of the 1949 census organised by the Department for Nature Protection of the State Forest Administration in Holland. C. D. Deane has given much information relevant to Ulster. Prof. Paul 'Espinasse has helped with the appendix on colour-changes. Sir Bartle Frere furnished an unpublished account of herons preying on waterfowl. Warren Fisher sent notes about New Zealand genera, P. A. D. Hollom unpublished records of unusual feeding habits. Prof. Hans Johansen provided invaluable notes on the intermediate races and also helped with information about Danish kitchen-middens. The late Gregory M. Mathews gave me his views concerning the nomenclature of the herons of Australia and New Guinea. Col. R. Meinertzhagen gave information concerning feather-parasites. Charles Oakey noted the position of the hind-toe in flight. Prof. Dr. G. J. van Oordt gave me his opinions concerning various aspects of the heron's status in the Netherlands. J. H. Owen gave me the benefit of his ripe experience with herons in Britain. J. Hughes Parry and the late Viscount Powerscourt supplied interesting comments upon specialised feeding habits. Major R. F. Ruttledge furnished valuable help with regard to the status of the species in Eire.

Ernst Schüz not only proved a mine of information about the movements of herons in Europe and out of it; but placed no restriction upon my use of the results of his great labour: moreover he supplied numerous German extracts and entrusted me with irreplaceable documents. I am grateful to Dr. Erwin Stresemann for copious notes on distribution copied by his own hand, and for his introduction to Dr. Schüz. Major J. W. Seigne supplied notes concerning out-of-season occupation of certain estuarine heronries. Miss Phyllis Barclay-Smith obtained for me certain obscure references from the library at the British Museum. The Count de Sainte Suzanne sent information about the historic French heronry on his former estates. J. Sneyd Taylor provided notes about African herons. Canon W. H. Thomas told of unrecorded marsh-nesting in England, H. J. Vermeulen drew attention to unusual feeding habits in Holland and Dr. G. M. Vevers furnished information about captive herons.

My researches into the pre-history, history and folk-lore of the heron have been advanced vastly by help received from Miss Dorothea M. A. Bate, Herbert Brewer, Prof. Henri Breuil, Dr. T. Gilchrist, the late Sir Hugh Gladstone, Dr. J. Wilfred Jackson and Eugene O'Mahony.

The Editorial Board of the *New Naturalist* have offered many suggestions to improve the text; I am grateful to Prof. Stamp for the suggestion of a map projection covering the whole area of the heron's world distribution; to Prof. Julian Huxley for reading the manuscript and offering much constructive criticism, and especially to James Fisher, whose tact has always tempered the advice of his editorial chair.

My friend Alfred Hazelwood has been helpful in many ways but most of all I have valued his critical faculty. I am grateful, too, for the forbearance and the criticism of my wife, who has given me her unstinted help during every stage of this work.

My indebtedness to the past and present owners of the Scarisbrick estates is such that, lacking their cooperation, I could not have undertaken this study without an enormous waste of energy and time: for I have always sought to confirm first-hand what others have seen, hoping that, occasionally, I might see some facet of behaviour overlooked by earlier observers. The more I read the more I realised how acute was the perception of those early naturalists who, right back to Aristotle, made observations about herons, some of which are only now being investigated, and it seems likely that the ornithologist of the future may pursue his studies as interpreter rather than as mere recorder of bird behaviour. If that be so he may well find, as Gilbert White so truly wrote, that "subjects of this kind are inexhaustible."

FRANK A. LOWE

CHAPTER I

DAM WOOD HERONRY

HERONS are fairly common birds, likely to be seen anywhere in Britain, except perhaps during the spring and early summer when they spend most of their time in woodland breeding-colonies. Their peculiar form, large size and apparently lumbering flight make them easily recognisable even to those who take no special interest in birds.

It is remarkable that there should be so little knowledge about a creature so conspicuous and so relatively common; though it can quite easily be understood that its way of life should have been adorned with fable and beset with prejudice. As far as I can discover, no complete study has been made of the way in which the life of *Ardea cinerea* is organised to meet the fundamental problems of survival and reproduction; although a good deal of work has been done in Britain and in Western Europe on different aspects of its natural history.

For over twenty years I have been watching and learning about herons in different places, but finally, for convenience, I concentrated on the colony in Dam Wood. The six-inch *Ordnance Survey* sheet, 1909 edition, Lancashire LXXXIII. N.E., shows Scarisbrick Hall, six miles from the coast, surrounded by plantations and farmlands. The Leeds and Liverpool canal fringes the estate on the south while the Wigan to Southport railway line is a mile to the north. Dam Wood Lane, now the main road, is a leafy avenue dividing the Scarisbrick demesne from Dam Wood, with Dam Lane running through to Dam Wood cottages and a rich agricultural tract stretching to the hills in the north-east. Nowadays there is little in the surrounding countryside which looks particularly attractive to herons; but the present generation of birds is

descended from a stock which occupied a very different terrain,
the state of which a hundred years ago can be imagined from the
local place-names. Snig Pot Brook and Perch Pool Lane are within
a mile of the heronry, while Black Moss, Jack's Mere, Merscar
Brook and Wholesome Brow Drain are suggestive of the fen-like
conditions which prevailed before drainage, railways and indus-
trialism changed the face of the country. The highest land in the
wood is little more than 60 feet above sea level. In [*40 & 41 Vict.*]
The Scarisbrick Estate Act, 1877 [*Ch.*6], a private act concerned with
the ordering of the estate, occur many references to the drainage
works of the past two decades. It should be remembered that until
about 1850 a large portion of Martin Mere, a great lake once
covering over 3,000 acres, still extended to within a mile of the
present Dam Wood heronry.

Dam Wood is private property and entry has always been
restricted to the use of occupational paths giving access to the
farms beyond. It is a mixed wood of about forty acres; that portion
favoured by the herons contains some indigenous birch, old oaks
and occasional rowans: there are many well-grown beeches, and
sycamores have been planted round the edges. A number of
spruces and larches have been introduced, and a species of exotic
pine (*Pinus excelsa*, a native of Nepal) which is of rather spreading
habit. There are many rhododendrons, which give sanctuary to
a host of thrushes and blackbirds. Here and there are drifts of
bluebells and trailing brambles. As is usual, beneath beech the
carpet is poor; but three-quarters of the wood has an undergrowth
of bracken so rampant that in late summer one has to wade
through a solid mass of spreading fronds.

Here herons have nested for at least a century and the colony
now usually consists of about twenty nests rather widely scattered.
In early spring motor-coaches run along Dam Wood Lane to
Southport; the village football or cricket team practise on a
neighbouring field; planes roar overhead, sometimes at low levels;
yet all day long herons can be seen from the roadway, through
the still naked branches, standing by their nests as completely
unconcerned as, presumably, were their ancestors a century
ago.

Frank A. Lowe

Plate 1a. The Dam Wood heronry. The standing-ground lies between the haystacks and the pit in the middle foreground

b. Heron feeding on Ribble marshes

John Kershaw

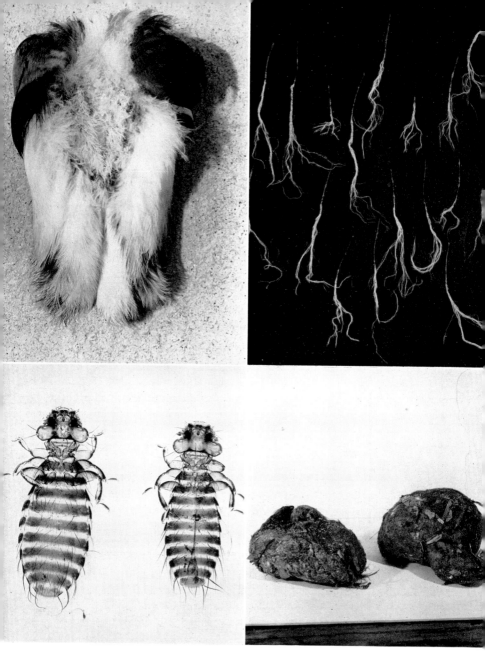

Plate 2a (top left). Breast of heron with contour feathers parted to show powder-down areas. *b (top right)*. Powder-down feathers. *c (lower left)*. Mallophaga from heron, *Ciconiphilus decimfasciatus* (Boisduval & Lacordaire, 1835). *d (lower right)*. Heron pellets of fur and beetle elytra. *(Photographs by Frank A. Lowe)*

Very little watching will reveal that Dam Wood and its immediate neighbourhood have features of special significance to the herons. Obviously the nesting trees have an ancestral hold on the birds. There is also a pine-tree of the greatest importance; its gnarled branches spread into a flat top, which for years has provided a neutral stance for any heron to rest or preen upon. This flat-topped pine is a vantage point from which the herons can view both their nesting trees and their standing ground on the adjacent field.

This standing-ground, as I have termed it, has its special significance. There the herons congregate early in the year before they go up to the tree-tops. In 1949 the first comers arrived on 8 February, and during the ensuing weeks the black earth generally showed up a group of herons. Later in the year the standing-ground recedes in importance, but even then, if agitated, a number of herons will go down to their old gathering-place. The standing-ground, the nesting-trees and the flat-topped pine are all intimately connected with the pattern of reproduction.

The terrain, which once must have been ideal, is still capable of supporting a considerable heron population. In the Hall Park is a large lake, now very shallow and gradually silting up, which holds a pair of mute swans and moorhens; but although herons visit the water it cannot be regarded as of great importance to them. The canal holds a multitude of fish, but little of its length is useful to the herons, as for the most part it lacks sloping banks and is often disturbed. However, from Perch Pool Lane to Snig Pot Brook the fields are well provided with pits, drains and brooks, mostly accessible and mostly undisturbed, abounding in fish and water-voles. Therein is the reason why herons are seldom seen foraging in the more extensive waters in the vicinity of Dam Wood. That too, is why they only occasionally feed on marine animals; for between Dam Wood and the shore, over Black Moss or Jack's Mere, are many tempting bits of water where voles make their toilet on the floating weeds while eels (snigs in Lancashire) are there for the taking.

Although something of the way a heron lives can be seen from the ground, the observer who wants to watch the progress of its nesting must go to the tree-tops. Twice I have erected observation posts in Dam Wood, in 1937 and again in 1948, when hide and nest were in exactly the same positions. Building a hide in the tree-tops presented the usual difficulties, most of which were overcome; but, to avoid scaring the herons, building was rather protracted. A platform was gradually erected 70 feet up a beech tree; then a superstructure was arranged piecemeal during two weeks. A forked branch made an excellent seat, there was a stand for a camera, one cord brought a rope ladder into operation, another served for a hoist. Although herons are fickle creatures, and there have been cases when disturbance has caused them to desert a colony, my birds accepted the hide without showing any signs of anxiety. I worked carefully and watched their reactions at every stage, ready to abandon the work; but their behaviour never made such a course seem necessary.

After the 1937 hide was in position, I was puzzled to find it more dilapidated and with more tie-strings missing at each visit. Later I discovered that tree-sparrows were taking them for nesting material, to their own nests inside the basements of the herons' nests. After a while the sparrows grew so bold as to pull strands of jute from the hide while I sat inside. I missed these little birds very much in 1948, when their numbers had been so greatly diminished by the preceding hard winter, and again in 1949 when there were still very few in Dam Wood. In 1937 a pair of starlings accumulated material in a fold of the sacking forming the hide, but a high wind blew it out and they did not persevere. In the same year a pair of stock-doves inspected the hide with no result, but in 1948 a pair made a nest inside the hide and laid two eggs. Unfortunately one rolled out as I entered one day and the doves deserted the other, but a month later laid again in the same place, successfully rearing a pair of squabs. In 1949 two successive broods of stock-doves were raised in the hide, which could not be dismantled until the last pair had fledged.

Periods in the hide were seldom tedious. Altogether I spent 100 hours in the first hide and some 300 in the second, my longest single watch extending over seven hours. On Easter eve I saw the sun go down and watched the dawn from the tree-tops. After that vigil there was no hour of the day and night that had not been included in one of my watches.

At the top of a high tree the watcher sees the world from a new angle: indeed he is in a new world, where finches and tits perch within inches of his face, and stock-doves sit calling from a nearby branch. Before the trees are in full leaf most of the herons' nests are visible from the hide, and there is nearly always something going on at one of them; maybe a bird will fly in with a ceremonial offering, or to relieve a sitting mate; maybe a skirmish with some intruder occurs to liven the scene. On the dead trunk of a birch a great spotted woodpecker is frequently to be seen and heard drumming. Sometimes lesser and greater black-backs fly across the heronry on their way to the shore; this usually starts a little argument between them and any approaching heron.

Even in earliest spring there is much activity in the heronry and this increases from the time the young hatch. It is interesting to review the nesting cycle, to recall how the community returns to the wood, how a peak of nesting activity is reached and how, having successfully reared another generation, the birds disperse and go their ways.

Throughout February herons come to the neighbourhood of the wood; the first may arrive as early as the eighth day, but the rest come in gradually—and during these first weeks spend more time on the standing-ground than in the wood. By the end of March a bird will be standing by most of the nests and a good many eggs will have been laid. On the first of April my hide was rocked by strong winds which did not seem to worry the herons at all. In the nearest swaying tree one bird stood by its nest while in another nest a bird was already incubating. Across a drain, by the edge of the wood overlooking the standing-ground, were two of the earliest nests; on each a bird was sitting with its mate in close attendance. Neither of the birds in the next tree to the hide had mates so attentive—perhaps because there were two nests in the one tree; for when a bird first arrived there was always a show of animosity from its neighbour. Close by Dam Wood Lane several other sitting or standing birds could be seen, all with their necks curved and heads resting on their shoulders. The flat-topped pine had several herons on it, desultorily preening, and others were to be seen rising from it or planing down to the standing-ground. As yet no young were out in any of the nests.

The hide is a pleasant place in May; the sun beats down on a shimmering landscape and the sound of bursting beech-buds is unbelievably loud. Young at various stages of growth lie or stand in the nests, of which all in sight, save one, are occupied. The empty nest has stood vacant for several years and, still intact after the buffeting winds and weather, now looks black as jet, in contrast to the occupied nests all liberally "whitewashed" by the young birds. Parent birds still stand by some of the nests and the clattering of the young is invariably heard at feeding times. The flat-topped pine is not so crowded as earlier in the year.

In June many young birds are standing on the edges of their nests, some engaged in vigorous exercises or preening: but adult herons spend less time at the nests. Dam Wood seems full of birds this month: the juveniles of first-broods of thrushes and blackbirds are everywhere; wrens have built in the roots of almost every upturned tree; willow-warblers, chiffchaffs and a pair of redstarts are all caterpillar-hunting. The carpet of the wood is full of biting flies but the top of the beech tree is quite free of them. A great outburst of activity in a nest of very big young near the edge of the wood threatens to end in tragedy; they have been venturesome, and have scattered over the thinner branches; one balanced on the extreme tip of a branch wildly beats its wings, somehow keeps its balance, and scrambles back to safety. This is the time when many over-venturesome young crash or are blown down.

July is the most exciting month of all. The once sprawling new-hatched young are grown as big as their parents: they stand in groups in the nests or in the trees and many are already strong on the wing. A larch, near the centre of the wood, has acquired a new significance as the standing-place of several young birds, which go there to digest their food, after receiving it in the nests, and to eject their pellets. The flat-topped pine is still the most popular tree with the old birds and some of the young also. One July day, three fully-grown young herons flew straight to the tree where I was hidden: from time to time they uttered low growling notes, quite unlike any sound produced by their parents. Soon these young birds were to leave the wood altogether, although as yet they were dependent on their parents. For close on half a year there had been heron activity centred round Dam Wood; but by late July the last of the birds will have left.

CHAPTER 2

PHYSICAL FEATURES

THE GENERAL IMPRESSION which the heron's appearance gives is one of great size, either standing with neck erect, when it reaches a height of fully three feet, or flying with a span of over five feet and a total wing area of almost four square feet. The heron may weigh as much as four and a half pounds or as little as three; an exceptionally low weight is probably due to loss from near-starvation in winter. It may surprise the reader to learn that the heron weighs so little. If a comparison is made on the ratio of surface area to weight, the whooper swan carries five times more weight per square foot of wing area than the heron; but the heron carries nearly four times more per square foot than the swallow. The heron is particularly slender, with its trunk compressed laterally so that the clavicle is very long. The breast-muscles, slighter than one might expect in a bird with such large wings, account for not quite 15 per cent of the total weight. In comparison, the breast-muscles of a barn-owl are approximately 10 per cent of its weight and those of the common snipe and rock-dove almost 30 per cent.

The neck has 19 cervical vertebrae, the sixth of which is longer than the others and is the fulcrum on which the neck moves; it is so articulated as to produce the sharp kink which is always apparent. There is a comparable condition in the cormorant and the gannet. When resting a heron carries its neck relaxed into a double curve, like the letter " S " horizontally compressed, the lower surface resting between the fork of the clavicles; when flying it draws its neck back in the same way, which distinguishes it at a glance from a swan, cormorant, stork or any other large, long-necked bird.

The gullet, which is frequently subjected to great distension

when food is swallowed or disgorged, is a large bag of extremely
elastic membrane which, in a dead bird, resumed its normal shape
after I had stretched it to eight times its normal diameter. The
entrance to the gullet is especially elastic and the organ is well
lubricated by secretions. Food is invariably swallowed with the
neck fully extended. R. Newstead first drew attention to the
structure of the neck and showed how when it was outstretched
the gullet and windpipe were perfectly straight although no
stretching would completely straighten the vertebrae. In the
resting position the central portion of the neck is arched although
the gullet does not follow the course of the vertebrae but, taking
the shortest path between gape and body cavity, is for a short
distance actually behind them. Herons are almost unique among
vertebrate animals in having a part of the backbone which pro-
trudes in front of their gullet.

A detailed anatomical study would be out of place here but
there are certain features in the heron's digestive tract and ancil-
lary glands which are indicative of the food it eats. It has a
relatively long gut, as is usual in grain or fish-eating birds, measuring seven feet, and two ducts pour into it the secretions of the mass
of pancreatic tissue which almost fills the duodenal loop. The large
size of the pancreas suggests that the heron is extraordinarily
capable of emulsifying fat; and, since the eel contains more fat
than any other freshwater fish, one might infer that the heron's
anatomy and physiology are specially adapted to digest eels.

A heron's bill measures from 5 to 5½ inches from the tip to the
gape, the mandibles closing in a long compressed cone of which
the greatest depth is little more than an inch, but this does not
greatly restrict what the bird can eat, for the gape is wide. The
nostrils are longitudinal slits situated within half-an-inch of the
forehead and communicating internally. Slight serrations on the
edges of the mandibles give a firm hold when food is seized. In
many birds which have wide gapes and capacious gullets the
tongue is very small or rudimentary: the free portion of a gannet's
tongue measures less than half-an-inch; this bird swallows fish as
it catches them and a long tongue would be an impediment: the
stork's tongue is rudimentary: the tongue of the flamingo is thick

and fleshy, like that of a duck. The heron, on the other hand, has a delicate tongue extending three-quarters the length of its mandibles. The heron kills its food before eating it; many kinds of food are taken and the tongue must be useful both in the catching and manipulation of prey.

The heron's foot is of special interest because of its adaptation to both wading and perching. A third of the tibia and the entire tarsus are covered with a horny integument of flat scales, which are large on the frontal surface of the tarsus and much smaller elsewhere; a similar pattern continues along the upper surface of the toes, which are long and slender with strong, arched and pointed claws. All the toes have a fleshy spreading undersurface; there is a basal web between the third and fourth toes only, which does not extend beyond the first joint and is continuous with the under-

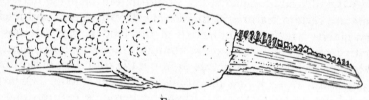

FIG. I
Third toe with pectinated claw

skin. The hind toe is long and set at the same level as the others. A remarkable feature of the foot is the claw of the third toe, the inner edge of which is flattened and serrated.

The extended integument, the wide-spreading toes with their expansive soles and web are clearly characteristics of a wading bird. Adaptation to arboreal habit is evidenced by the length of the hind toe and its position on the same level as the others (it is usually set higher in wading birds), thereby investing the foot with some of the grasping ability of the passerine foot.

A pectinated claw is found, as well as in herons, in bitterns, gannets, cormorants and the insectivorous nightjars; clearly it has been evolved independently more than once. As far as the heron is concerned the pectinated claw serves several purposes, although there can be no doubt that, as with the other birds,* its primary function is for preening. The serrations are in effect a comb; after an eel has been eaten any slime left on the bird's plumage is liberally dusted with powder-down grains to reduce its stickiness, so that it can easily be removed by the claw. The heron may use the claw for other purposes such as holding a fish, as an aid when walking over slippery stones, or as a tooth-comb to remove biting lice, but undoubtedly its main function is to remove eel-slime.

The arrangement of the feather-tracts and intervening spaces differs from family to family, the heron being notable for narrow feather-tracts, wide spaces on the neck and the possession of powder-down patches. The narrow lateral feather-tracts of the neck, with spaces on dorsal and ventral surfaces, enable herons to fold their necks compactly in the characteristic "S" formation.

The heron has three pairs of so-called powder-down areas, well covered by the contour-feathers; there are two large tracts on the hips, two smaller tracts in the region of the clavicles, sited between the ventral feather-tracts; and a third pair of rather narrow patches is sited along the groins. The skin of a newly-killed heron is dark beneath these patches, owing to the great congestion of the shafts, which are bright yellow, and support numerous fine grey filaments, devoid of lateral offshoots. These filaments are so friable that they disintegrate if rubbed between the fingers, which they leave coated with an adhesive film of amorphous material. The powder they thus form is bluish-white, waxy to the touch, and will neither dissolve nor mix with water; with it the heron liberally coats its plumage when preening. Its main function is to cleanse the feathers of the slime of eels and other fish.

Although the shafts of the contour-feathers are all embedded in a comparatively small portion of the heron's skin they are so arranged that the body is clothed in a sober dress of blue-grey, white and black. An adult has a whitish head with a glossy black band running from behind each eye extended as a long pendant crest. Part of the black crest on the hinder portion of the head is obscured by a number of long white feathers growing from the

*I have seen a nightjar "combing" its nasal bristles to remove fragments of insects.

crown. The black crest feathers are lanceolate, the shorter ones having long free rami. The two longest, which grow from the base of the crown, may measure, according to H. F. Witherby, from 80 to 210 mm. On the average the plumes of the males are longer than those of the females, but this has no value as a means of sexing individual herons, as many a female has longer plumes than some males, for the plumes increase with each successive moult until they attain their maximum size; it does not follow that birds of the same age and sex will have plumes of identical length, since there is a good deal of individual variation.

The heron's neck is pale buff-grey on its ventral surface, below a white chin: its throat has an interesting pattern of black spots on a white ground, caused by the feathers at the ventral edges of the lateral neck-tracts being particoloured. These, rather curiously, have the inner webs black and the outer webs white. They increase progressively in size from the upper throat downwards and terminate as elongated, almost lanceolate plumes. It is significant that the broken line of the black and white on the heron's ventral surfaces is on that part of the bird which would be visible to aquatic prey; so long as it remains motionless, the outline of its form, broken by this ruptive pattern, must be scarcely visible to its victims.

The centre of the breast from the wishbone, the belly and under tail-coverts are white; the leg-feathers are whitish tinged with buff. The under-sides of the wings and the flanks are blue-grey, as are the twelve tail-feathers. The upper wing-coverts, bastard wing and primaries are blue-black. The primaries are emarginated, or cut away to allow locally increased air passage, and their webs, especially on the inner side, have a very high sheen, which, although giving the feathers the appearance of having been waxed, has a structural basis.

The featherless soft parts of a heron alter in colour with age; their variation during development is described in a later chapter. Both mandibles of the adult are yellowish although their shade may vary from straw colour to a yellow-brown. In spring, the mandibles may assume a deep pink hue.* The lores also are

*See Appendix 2.

yellowish, tinged green round the eyes. The iris is yellow. Legs and feet are dull brown, the frontal scales (with a smoother surface) appearing darker than the rest.

Apart from the wear on the powder-downs, which is a continuous process of breaking down and replacement extending from the heron's second month throughout its life, the fully adult bird undergoes one complete annual moult, starting normally in July and ended by November. The birds sometimes drop the third or fourth pair of tail feathers before the end of June while they are still attending young. Some start to lose their primaries about the same time, but those occupying the small late-built nests, presumably birds nesting for the first time, do not start to shed their quills so soon as the other birds. Another change in the plumage of the adult heron concerns its crest, which, far from being fully developed in February, only attains its greatest length by April.

Aberrations from this colour and pattern are rare; but albino birds and cases of dilute colouration have been reported on at least four occasions during this century from various parts of Britain.

Some knowledge of the bird's sensorial perceptions can be gathered by observing its reactions to sights, sounds and smells. The eyes are relatively small with flattish lenses but the bird's diurnal sight is excellent. As in all birds the movement of the eye within the orbit is limited. Raptorial birds have their eyes directed forwards whereas most species have the advantage of a larger field of vision (at the sacrifice of stereoscopic sight) by having their gaze directed sideways. The heron effects a compromise in that its eyes, although set well to the sides of its head, are directed slightly forward. Thus within a narrow angle at least, due to the overlapping field of vision of the two eyes, it has the advantage of stereoscopic sight. This arrangement meets the heron's requirements admirably: it has monocular vision over a wide lateral field and a restricted backward and downward view with binocular vision over a limited frontal field, so that it does not risk losing sight of some fast-moving prey through having to make a parallax estimate before seizing it.

A heron's hearing is acute; the snapping of a twig by a distant visitor is immediately recognised above the familiar creakings of the tree-tops and the sound's origin instantly located. Herons rely very little on the sense of smell: the olfactory lobe and the sense of smell are, as in most birds, poorly developed, for birds brooding close downwind have remained ignorant of my presence, even a cloud of tobacco smoke blown over them passing apparently unnoticed.

The physical features of the heron show specialisation in two rather different directions, to aid the catching of aquatic prey and to fit it for an arboreal life. Its long legs, semi-binocular vision, powder-down, 'comb' claw and grasping toes show adaptation for its particular mode of life, but it has retained enough generalised structure to enable it to live outside the limitations imposed by the 'perfection' of specialisation.

CHAPTER 3

WORLD DISTRIBUTION AND POPULATIONS

THE HERON, *Ardea cinerea*, (with three recognised subspecies or geographical races which replace each other in various parts of its range) has a total range extending throughout the Palaearctic and Ethiopian regions. It succeeds because it is "euryplastic" (Huxley, 1942) as regards climate and physiography, which means that it is not limited by adaptation to any very particular environment. It occurs almost continuously over the continents of Europe, Asia and Africa, having penetrated as far as 77° 30'N and 34°S. Except as an occasional wanderer it does not occur west of about 17°W: eastwards it is certainly found to 150°E. While its density in Europe is greatest within a few hundred feet of sea-level, it may occasionally be seen on the highest mountain lakes and the eastern race has been found at 11,000 feet.

The heron's most northerly breeding place is Skjervoy, in Norway, 70°N. The northern limit in Sweden is 65° 45'N, in the western parts of the U.S.S.R. about 60°N, and by the Yenesei River 55°N. Temperature tends to be progressively depressed along the northern latitudes as they cross more easterly meridians; and the northern breeding limit coincides with an isotherm drawn across Europe and Asia to mark the mean annual temperature of 32°F. The heron has, however, been observed breeding at Yakutsk, 62°N in East Siberia, where the annual mean temperature is only about 12°F. This can be explained as in that region there is such a violent change in the direction of the summer isotherms that from June to September it is warmer than in many places farther west on the same parallel. The absolute limiting factor to the heron's northerly distribution is ice; it cannot live permanently in regions of prolonged or extensive ice but it takes advantage of warmer weather and temporarily increases its range by following the thaw to higher latitudes.

Herons of the western race occur from north of the Arctic Circle to the Cape. Along the southern limits temperature varies little more than 10°F above or below the mean average of about 60°F; indeed, in these latitudes seasonal movements may not be influenced by temperature.

To the west the heron is bounded by the Atlantic Ocean; and its eastern race, not having been known to cross the rather narrow Bering Strait to Alaska, is thus bounded by the Pacific. In America its place is taken by the Great Blue Heron, *Ardea herodias*, a replacing species so closely related that it is most probably a subspecies which has achieved specific rank, the two together forming a 'superspecies'.

There are records of herons having wandered far beyond their normal bounds, three having been reported in Greenland between 1765 and the present day. There are no reports of herons having nested or wintered in Iceland, where their occurrence is regarded as accidental, but there are a few every year, and they are universally known even in the north of that island. There are many records of herons, mostly juveniles, visiting the Faeroes. There is a regular passage each year to the Faeroese island of Nolsoy, usually in parties of three to five, whereas at one time the heron was believed to be only an occasional visitor.

In Scandinavia in Dresser's time the heron had not been observed north of the Lofoten Islands, but now, almost certainly as a result of the change of climate of the last 50-100 years, the whole of Scandinavia is within its range (an immature heron was shot in the Varanger Peninsula in East Finmark), besides being the only region in which it has bred north of the Arctic Circle. Breeding colonies are sparsely scattered within the littoral belt and up to a dozen miles inland, the greatest numbers nesting near the coasts of Stavanger and Bergen in Norway and in southern Sweden. Inland breeding has been recorded from Gudbrandsdalen (Norway, 61° 30'N 10°E), but most of the birds seen inland are on their passage south during September and October, when they some-

times number a hundred together (Løvenskiöld, 1946), or returning in March. Herons winter in Norway only on the south-west
coast.

In Finland also the heron's status has changed considerably
with the change of climate during the last half-century. Formerly
it was considered extremely rare and Dresser gives one doubtful
record of breeding at Taipale, in the south. K. E. Kivirikko states
that what was probably the first Finnish heronry was established
in 1847 in Halikko, near the present eastern border; but in the
last few years there has been nesting every spring, chiefly in the
Karelian Isthmus. Herons have been seen by the shores of the
Gulf of Bothnia. They do not arrive in Finland until April and
leave again in September and October.

Herons are still very rare in Estonia, much more numerous in
Latvia, and common in suitable conditions in Lithuania. For
Poland no precise data are available, although here, as in south
Russia, the birds are common in favourable localities, as many as
fifty together having been seen in the Uman district.

The heron is a summer visitor to Denmark, arriving in March
and April and leaving in September and October; its status here
is thus different from its status in Britain: although Denmark lies
between the same latitudes as Britain from Newcastle to Aberdeen,
the winters are much colder. Throughout Holland and Belgium
the heron is very common, although much more numerous in
Holland. In the Low Countries herons are to be seen throughout
the year, although there is a considerable migration. In France a
small breeding stock is augmented in autumn by an influx of birds
of more northerly origin passing through the country or going to
its southern provinces. To the Channel Islands the heron is an
occasional wanderer.

A study of distribution in the Iberian peninsula reveals various
complexities. Many birds from northern Europe winter there,
while others pass through to winter farther south. Birds from
Denmark have been found as far south as Badajos and Cordoba
between August and December. In Andalusia, Abel Chapman
remarked that "when summer heats provoke miasma and fetid
airs, languor-laden, from the morass, the herons congregate" for

nesting purposes: this and other observations show clearly that the summer population is vastly increased by immigrants. In winter, large numbers have been seen near Gibraltar, and the Balearic Isles have supported birds from Germany and France. Spain is nearly the geographical centre of the heron's north-south range and it is inevitable that there should be some overlapping and crossing of the movements of different populations. The heron arrives in Portugal in September and leaves in March; throughout the winter the species is commonly seen on the lagoons, in the marshes, and by the largest rivers; but by the time the purple herons (*A. purpurea*) arrive to breed the common herons have already left. There is no proof, in fact, that the heron breeds in Portugal, or in any part of Spain save the south.

Considerable numbers of herons nest in north and central Italy, but not in the south, although they are common there in winter. There is no obvious topographical or climatic reason to account for non-breeding in southern Italy; but a possible explanation is advanced in Chapter 9, connected with the rhythm of migration. The heron occurs on passage and in winter in Sicily and in Malta, where it may be seen, too, in spring and summer; Corsica and Sardinia support a small resident population.

Widely distributed throughout Germany, the heron is mostly migratory in the north and to some extent sedentary in the south. A large breeding population is contained in the Balkans: it has been recorded as numerous at Corfu and in all parts of the mainland of southern Greece, where it arrives a little in advance of the purple heron. After a short stay it moves north to breed, returning to the south in August. Considerable numbers nest in Thrace and in winter many are found in the islands of the Aegean between Greece and Asia Minor.

The southern limit of the heron's breeding range is in the region of 34°S. As the distribution given in *The Handbook of British Birds* is unduly compressed it may convey a wrong impression of the heron's status in South Africa, where it breeds commonly, there being several colonies close to Cape Town where it resorts to mixed heronries in tall trees. It bred formerly in reed-beds on the Cape Flats. It nests in the reed-beds round Lake Nyassa, occurs

Plate 3. Portrait of heron with young

Plate 4a. Nuptial display

b. Aggressive display

in both North and South Rhodesia, and is common on the Barotse Plain. East Africa does not contain as dense a population as West, but some ten pairs nesting in borassus-palms at Korkora provide proof of breeding in Kenya. It is rather scarce throughout Kenya and Uganda, while in Abyssinia its place is taken to a great extent by the black-necked heron (*A. melanocephala*).

Common herons have been recorded in West Africa, from the Cape Verde islands along the littoral belt of Senegal, Gambia, Portuguese Guinea, Sierra Leone, Liberia, the Ivory Coast and Gold Coast, through Dahomey and Nigeria to the Cameroons. There is proof of breeding in Nigeria, where it is widely distributed. In some places herons penetrate far inland; according to Bannerman one such locality is Bornu, the part of Nigeria farthest from the sea. Herons are more numerous north of latitude 11°N.

It is common on the central plateau of West Africa, where it haunts open grassland, taking frogs and grasshoppers from the farms. "Wherever there is water, along the streams and rivers, by pools and water-holes, and in the reed-covered swamps, the Grey Heron may be found. It is frequently to be seen, too, and especially in the dry season, when the crops have been cleared and the grass is short, stalking deliberately over the stubbles or waiting for insects in the dry fadamma" (Hutson & Bannerman). In winter, herons haunt the Niger in the southern Sahara, where a dozen have been seen together in the company of ibises: at the same season there is a concentration on Lake Chad which disperses before May. Quite the largest congregation of passage herons yet noticed was described by K. M. Guichard who saw, in the flooding zone on the River Niger in the French Sudan, some 300 birds "gathered in a dense flock on the bank of the Barra-Issa" . . . on 11 October 1943 near Sarafere, 70 miles from Timbuctoo.

The resident heron population of North Africa is augmented by immigrants from Europe and in winter the population of Morocco is at its peak, although there are some birds all the year round about Tangier. In Algeria herons abound on all the lakes; occasionally they are found in ditches and salt-marshes in winter and in March have been recorded in the Algerian Sahara. Resident in Tunisia, the birds are largely marsh-breeders near

c

Bizerta and Mater, and at times the local population is greatly swelled by an influx of passage-migrants. Herons occur on passage and as residents in Tripolitania, Lybia and in Egypt, where they nest at Giza and on the islands in the Red Sea. An autumn passage in the Nile Delta extends from early September to November, and a spring passage from February to April—"on one occasion a flock of over 100 were seen in the Fayum flying north on March 14" (Meinertzhagen). Herons are to be found on the sandbanks throughout Egypt and Nubia, often in considerable numbers, with spoonbills *Platalea leucorodia*, pelicans *Pelecanus onocrotalus*, and other birds. In the desert they hunt lizards and beetles, and probably the mice and toads which abound there (Nicoll).

Throughout Africa, then, wherever there is suitable territory, herons may at some season be found which are identical with those that breed in Great Britain. In the Atlantic Islands nesting has been recorded in most of the Canaries, while vagrants have occurred in Madeira and the Azores, which are the extreme westerly limit of the heron's distribution.

So far, the herons to which I have been referring all belong to the western race, *Ardea cinerea cinerea*. This geographical race is common all the year round in Turkey, is prevalent the length of the Red Sea coast, through Arabia to the Persian Gulf, occurs in Iran and moves into Baluchistan and Sind in winter. As we have seen, it is the race which inhabits Africa. It is this typical race which inhabits Zanzibar and Pemba in the Indian Ocean, which are zoo-geographically a part of the mainland, but is replaced by another subspecies *A. c. firasa* on Madagascar.

The eastern race *A. c. jouyi* extends westwards to the islands in the Persian Gulf and occurs across Persia, Transcaspia, India and eastwards to China and Japan, to Sumatra, Java, Borneo, and more rarely to the Philippines and New Guinea. While it is impossible to estimate numbers of these eastern populations there is no doubt that they exceed those of the west.

So numerous are herons in India that immigrant flocks of up to a hundred birds in February augment the resident population of Sind, where the fishermen catch them for food: around the fishing villages herons may be seen in boats, where they are kept tethered by one leg either as decoys or to fatten. Confusion as to which race inhabits India has arisen because these immigrants are of the western race (given by *The Handbook of British Birds* as that typical of India), whereas the resident population is certainly of the eastern race.

Throughout China herons are abundant; in winter large flocks visit the tidal areas and mud-flats near Hongkong. The species is common in the Central Provinces but the greatest concentration is in the south-east. Some of these birds are remarkably fearless in their choice of a nesting site: "In the centre of Samshui City . . . is an immense and aged tree [in which] a large heronry is situated. There is another heronry at Shiu Hing City, in the Magistrate's garden where the birds are never disturbed, and in this case the nests are placed in scattered banyan trees, and like those at Samshui are in the upper and dead branches" (Vaughan & Jones, 1913). The nests in these colonies were very small when their owners started to lay but further material was added as incubation advanced. Similar instances of fearlessness in the choice of sites by herons in Europe are provided by purple herons and common herons in Holland, both species having established flourishing heronries in zoological gardens, while wild herons used to come to the roof of the big aviary in the London zoo. Nowhere in the west has there been such a colony as that described by Sir Evan James in Manchuria, where, near the junction of the rivers Sungari and Sunchiang, "thousands of herons and cormorants were nesting together in the willow trees."

In Japan and the islands of the Pacific the heron occurs in much smaller numbers than in continental Asia. It is probably only a vagrant to New Guinea and there is no authentic record of its having occurred in Australia. There is no evidence to support the statement, quoted by W. R. B. Oliver, that it occurred once in New Zealand, "an example having been caught on board a schooner off the east coast about 1898."

Subspecific Differentiation

It is not remarkable that in a species like the heron, which is distributed over such great tracts of the earth's surface, racial differentiation should have arisen. In some species populations are separable as clear-cut geographical races. There are, however, many species without such striking differentiation. To quote Mayr, "they show gliding intergradation between the characters of the individuals of one population as well as between neighbouring populations and subspecies. This so-called continuous variation affects most frequently the total size of the animal, or the relative and absolute size of parts, or various shades of colouration, characters which are naturally prone to vary geographically." Huxley has called these character-gradients clines; and at each end of the cline there are often forms which differ as do sharply marked subspecies which are the result of isolation.

The common heron of Europe (typical locality Sweden), *Ardea c. cinerea,* differs chiefly in the colour of the wing-coverts from the common heron of eastern Asia *A. c. jouyi,* so named in 1907 by Austin H. Clark from skins obtained by P. L. Jouy in Korea. The wing-coverts of the eastern race are much paler than those of the western race—indeed they are almost ashy-white.

There has been much uncertainty as to whether the herons in India belong to the eastern or western race, and I am grateful to the authorities of the British Museum (Natural History) for allowing me to handle the relevant material. Undoubtedly the race occurring throughout India, Pakistan and Burma is *A. c. jouyi.* I have examined skins from the Makran coast of Baluchistan, from Ouhd in the United Provinces and from the Upper Chindwin in Burma and although the specimens had been assembled from a range of over 2,000 miles there were only the slightest shades of difference between them. The European race is said to be a casual straggler in winter to Sind and Baluchistan in the north-west (E. C. Stuart Baker) and a skin taken at Quetta at 5,500 feet in the month of October is certainly *cinerea* rather than *jouyi.*

The area of intergradation occupies a wide belt between the two distinct terminal subspecies. Birds from Western Siberia are generally a little lighter than birds from Western Europe. In the Bird Room I arranged a series of skins in sequence according to the longitude of the place whence they had been taken; at one end of the series was a dark-mantled bird from Skye, at the other end birds from North China and Korea, which were indistinguishable from each other, with very light mantles. The skin of an adult male with particularly good plumes from the Persian shores of the Caspian was certainly an intermediate, its dorsal side being much lighter than the typical European bird but darker than those from the Far East.

To supplement my observations Prof. H. Johansen has most kindly given me his conclusions after comparing the specimens in the Zoological Museum of the Academy of Science at Leningrad with others from Western Siberia. He found that skins from Alashan, Nanshan and Gobi were much lighter on the dorsal side than any of the others; very slightly darker were skins from Ussuri and Transbaikalia and Yakutia; most skins from Turkestan, the Khirgiz Steppes and West Siberia, while a little lighter than European ones, are definitely closer to typical *A. c. cinerea* than to *A. c. jouyi;* although *some* skins from these areas bore a certain resemblance to skins from Transbaikalia. The Turkestan, West and Central Siberian populations are all intermediate.

The Eastern and Western races of the heron, though termini of a cline, are sufficiently distinct to be classed as subspecies. Two theories have been put forward to explain this gradation. Either it is an adjustment to continuous environmental, climatic or other gradients over the distance covered by the cline; or it could be that the gene-flow between the two parts of the stock had been interrupted during the last glacial period. When the ice which had driven them apart receded northwards from Siberia the two parts of the stock, which had acquired different character-combinations during their isolation, but were still capable of interbreeding, would extend their range until they came together again. If that were so then the situation would represent a belt of hybridisation between the two races.

That such zones of hybridisation exist as the result of the recession of the ice age is abundantly demonstrated. Dementiev listed 36 Russian species having such zones in Western Siberia and elsewhere. A familiar example is provided by the carrion-crow *Corvus corone* and the hooded crow *C. cornix* with the zone of hybrids between them. The subspecies of the long-tailed tit *Aegithalos caudatus* and the bullfinch *Pyrrhula pyrrhula* are further examples of the results of two divergent forms interbreeding when they meet again (Huxley).

One might assume that the character-gradient of the heron was merely another example of the effects of ice-age isolation, but Mayr stresses that in a typical hybrid zone not only "the change from one character combination (subspecies a) to the other combination (subspecies b) is very abrupt," but also that, in the corridor between the two subspecies, the hybrid population is very variable with a majority of the intermediates but with individuals indistinguishable from either subspecies. This does not appear to be so in the case of the heron.   The occurrence of a darker-mantled bird than is usual at any particular meridian is, I believe, explained by dispersal, in the way that individuals of the western race or more westerly intermediates are found in north-west India along with a population predominantly of the eastern race.

There is one other subspecies *A. c. firasa* Hartert, which is larger than either of the continental forms. It is the product of geographical isolation and is confined to Madagascar, Aldabra and probably the Comoros; and is therefore of course not connected by a cline with any other race.

POPULATION DENSITIES, FLUCTUATIONS AND CHANGES

Few species provide more satisfactory material for the census-taker than the heron. Its nest is large, conspicuous and generally grouped with others in a conveniently small area. But while every census so far has dealt satisfactorily with tree-nesting birds, the other two kinds of heronry have been neglected. In parts of its range, notably in Norway and north-west Scotland, the heron is a cliff-nester; and over a greater area, especially in eastern and southern Europe, heronries are found in the marshes.

There are insufficient data to assess with accuracy the number of common herons in the world. Only in western Europe have nest-counts been made on any considerable scale. Throughout the rest of the species' range it is usually possible to find reference to the heron's numerical strength in general terms, and there is no doubt that the eastern populations outnumber those of the west. Nowhere in Europe during the present century has there been a parallel to a colony in the Vale of Kashmir where there were 47 nests in a single plane-tree, or to one in China with 60 nests in one camphor tree.

Information concerning the density of birds is gained from nest-counting and it is to this method that we owe our knowledge of the number of herons in certain parts of the species' range, and something of the fluctuations and the movement of populations. While the figures thus obtained may be reasonably accurate as estimates of breeding populations they take no account of the considerable non-breeding stock. We may conclude therefore that all nest-counts are likely to give underestimates.

In 1927 in Denmark 1,400 nests were counted in 28 colonies; whereas in 1944-45 the count showed that not only had the number of nests increased to 1,600 but the number of heronries had risen to 52 and there were 5 single nests. Although the actual population had not increased by more than the normal annual fluctuation, the average size of heronry had fallen from 50 to 30 nests. In 1945 the two largest heronries had 100 and 144 nests respectively against 175 in the largest colony in 1927. We see in Denmark not a decline in the heron population but a redistribution brought about by changing woodland conditions. The colonies have become more scattered and recently new sites have been occupied in Jutland, where until lately none bred.

In Holland there has been not merely a redistribution but a decline in the heron population. Its status suffered very severely as a result of timber-felling during the German occupation, and of damage to the nesting trees by inundations. The regulation of streams and marsh reclamation have also changed the character of the regions where herons catch their prey. Industrial pollution, severe winters and persecution have combined to reduce the number of herons in Holland during the last 15 years by 44 per cent. The vast colony at Gooilust is greatly decreased and many heronries in the Province of Zeeland have been destroyed. Between the

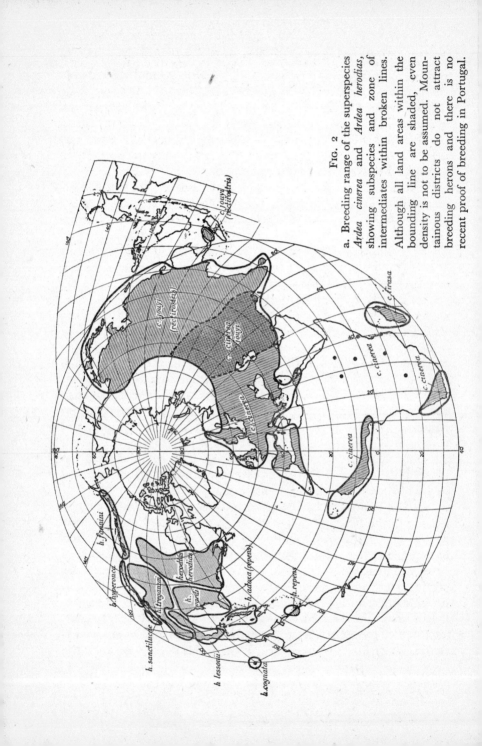

Fig. 2

a. Breeding range of the superspecies *Ardea cinerea* and *Ardea herodias*, showing subspecies and zone of intermediates within broken lines. Although all land areas within the bounding line are not to be assumed. Mountainous districts do not attract breeding herons and there is no recent proof of breeding in Portugal.

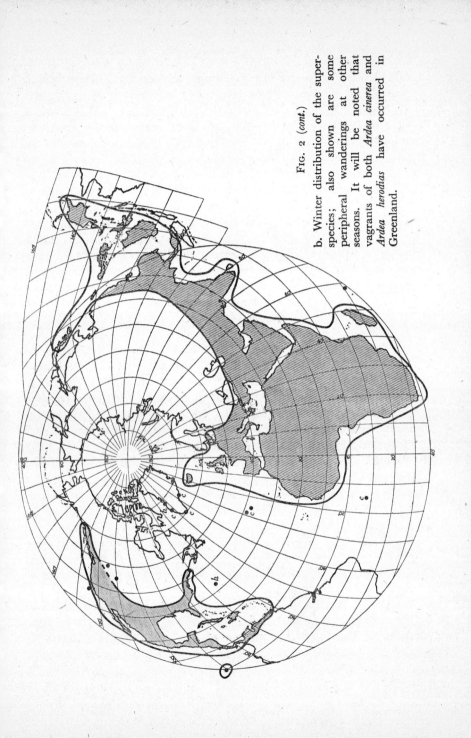

FIG. 2 (*cont.*)

b. Winter distribution of the super-species; also shown are some peripheral wanderings at other seasons. It will be noted that vagrants of both *Ardea cinerea* and *Ardea herodias* have occurred in Greenland.

two World Wars the largest colony in western Europe was at Gooilust in Noord-Holland which, in 1925, contained 1,035 nests. To appreciate this figure it may help if we realise that it is over a quarter of the entire breeding stock of herons in England and Wales together (3,800) and four times the heron population of the whole of Wales. Gooilust provided a good example of the speed with which a great colony can be built up: the first pair bred there in 1896 and within 30 years the colony had increased to over 1,000 pairs; in 1936 there were 638 nests and in 1949 only 175. Before the Nazi occupation, there were in Holland about 7,000 nests, approximately twice as many as in England. A census taken in 1949 returned 4,540 nests, which still represents a breeding density far greater than in any other European country (see Table 1, p. 30). I was much interested by the number of nests I saw in poplars in North Holland, while in the Muy, on Texel, birds were nesting in the reed-beds, a site not common in Western Europe.

France provides a further illustration of the decline of a once great and historic heronry. The heronry at Ecury-le-Grand, near Champigneul, Marne, formerly the property of the Count de Sainte Suzanne, contained in 1897 no less than 220 nests. By 1928 this number had fallen to about 30 and in 1948 the Count informed me that the heron had become " very scarce in that place." This heronry, now on the verge of extinction, although once the largest in France, was marked on a plan of the property dated 1682, and according to one authority was in existence in 1388. In 1928 there were two heronries in France each containing 100 nests, while the total population of that country was estimated at no more than some 350 pairs.

Heronries in France, situated mostly on private estates, are protected or harassed according to the interests of the respective proprietors, but during the Second World War a great increase in the number of common herons was noted. J. Berlioz, of the National Museum of Natural History in Paris, attributed this to the imposition of a ban on fire-arms during the war years, as since the ban was lifted the number of herons has rapidly declined: this decrease may also have been hastened by severe drought, particularly during 1947. It is significant, too, that the wartime increase in France coincided with a period of decrease in Holland.

No census of Italian heronries is available, but observations were made by Oddi and Moltoni in the Province of Piedmont during the years 1930-33. At a heronry at Casalino in the Novaro district, common herons had the place to themselves and, very remarkably in Western Europe, as many as 20 nests were in one tree. A second colony, at Greggio in the Vercelli district, was a mixed heronry with the night-heron predominating, for out of an incomplete count of 580 nests only 45 belonged to the common heron; little egrets and squacco herons were also sparsely represented.

Although German ornithologists have made provincial nest-counts these have not been synchronous; but a synthesis of the data reveals interesting features. There is a great disparity in the size of the heronries from province to province, the average varying between almost 100 nests in the Rhineland to a modest 12 in Schleswig-Holstein. The average size for the whole of Germany is about 30 nests, with the largest heronry of about 400 (one of the largest in Western Europe) in the East Friesland Luetelsburger Forst. There are close on 10,000 nests in what was the territory of the Third Reich.

To conclude this survey it is appropriate that the heron populations of each country wherein a nest-count has been made be reduced to common terms. A convenient formula is to relate the number of nests to the area of the land concerned. Because the various counts listed were not all made at the same time the comparisons are only approximate. The figures for England and Wales are discussed in some detail in the next Chapter.

COMPARATIVE DENSITY OF SOME WEST EUROPEAN
COMMON HERON POPULATIONS

	Estimated no. of nests	Year or years of estimate	Area of country in square miles	No. of pairs to 100 square miles
ENGLAND & WALES	3800	1928 & later normal years	58340	6.5
HOLLAND	4540	1949	12579	36.0
BELGIUM	300	1928	11755	2.6
GERMANY	10000	1938	180985	5.5
FRANCE	350	1928	212659	0.2
DENMARK	1600	1945	16576	9.6
TOTAL	20590		492894	4.2

CHAPTER 4

THE HERON POPULATION OF BRITAIN

HERONS are generally distributed over the British Isles in that they are likely to turn up in any place at any time, for they haunt the wildest parts of the country and yet come down to fish in town garden pools. In terrain like the marshland of Suffolk or the meres of Cheshire, one or more may be seen almost any day of the year. There are other places where the presence of the birds is more seasonal; for instance they pass over my house in a Lancashire town most frequently in winter and on many of the ponds in west Lancashire where they feed throughout the spring and summer their occurrence is irregular in autumn and winter. It is scarcely possible to journey across Britain without seeing a heron by some waterside, though the ease with which they are recognised is apt to give an exaggerated impression of their numerical strength.

The earliest attempts to count the heron population of Britain were not sufficiently well organised to give accurate statistics. The best of these was made in 1872 by J. E. Harting who said, in his preamble to the list published in *The Zoologist*, "Many doubtless will be surprised to learn that within the limits of the British Isles the existence of more than 200 heronries has been lately established." In the *Report on the "British Birds" census of Heronries, 1928*, 216 occupied heronries were found in England and 39 in Wales; the following year a supplementary report listed several sites previously overlooked and almost a dozen newly founded. Subsequent additions and subtractions have been made during the intervening years, but the breeding population of the heron in England and Wales (normally around 3,800 nests) is now contained in some 260 heronries.

The 1928 report includes a summary tabulating the counties of England and Wales, with their acreages, number of heronries and breeding populations. None were recorded for Rutland or Cambridgeshire, but the omission of Cambridgeshire was an error, for a flourishing colony of some score of pairs had been known near Wisbech for at least fifty years. In 1931 a site near Mepal, extinct since about 1885, was recolonised by 10 pairs; in 1932 three colonies contained 44 nests; in 1937 they contained 56; in 1938 only two heronries were counted and they contained 71 nests; by 1942 a great decline had taken place and only 29 nests were counted in the four known Cambridgeshire heronries, but the following year there was a partial recovery to 48 nests.

In Derbyshire there was known only a single pair and in Gloucestershire one heronry with two nests. Norfolk had both the greatest number of nests (331-51) and the largest number of colonies (19), thereby exceeding Cumberland (18) by a single colony although containing thrice the number of nests. Herons now breed in all the counties of England and Wales except Rutland. Shooting prevents any increase in Derbyshire but in Gloucestershire two new heronries have been established since this census.

Birds, however, do not respect county boundaries. Distribution and density are determined principally by the natural features of the land. Heronries are not numerous in mountainous country, whereas a long river, with its intricate system of tributaries, may carry a great number. Industrial areas, with congested human populations and often polluted waters, naturally hold fewer heronries than sparsely inhabited rural districts, although a heronry may thrive in a highly populated place. The following table illustrates the relationship of breeding density to these features. The figures are based on the 1928 census, amended by the inclusion of the Cambridgeshire heronries, as this is the most complete nest-count yet made. It must be borne in mind that the number of nests does not of necessity agree with the number of pairs of herons, as some heronries contain unoccupied nests. To avoid overestimating, great care should be taken to ensure that only those containing eggs or young are counted. The names of

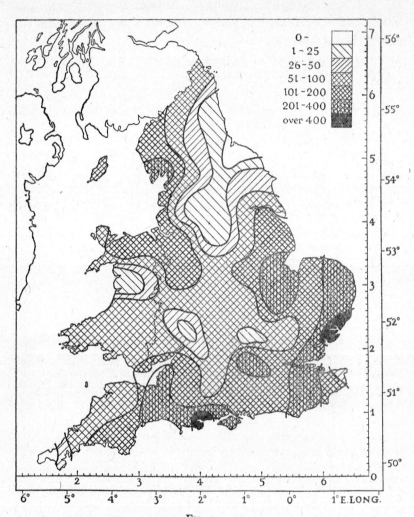

FIG. 3

Density of heron (smoothed) in nests per 100 square miles, assuming range of 10–20 km. from nests

the principal organisers of the original nest-counts, together with some of those who are still actively counting, are added after the survey of each province.

THE HERONRIES OF ENGLAND AND WALES
RELATED TO TOPOGRAPHY

Province	No. of heronries	Total no. of nests	Average size of colony
S-W Peninsula	37	536	14.0
English Channel	24	268–276	11.3
Thames *drainage area*	25	585	23.4
Ouse *drainage area*	40	773	19.3
Severn *drainage area*	22	248	11.3
Trent *drainage area*	16	250	15.6
Humber *drainage area*	12	120	10.0
Mersey *drainage area*	8	173	21.6
Tyne *drainage area*	9	62	7.0
English Lakes (& I.O.M.) ..	27	260	9.6
South Wales	24	170	7.0
North Wales	15	105	7.0

S-W Peninsula

Herons abound throughout Somerset, Devon and Cornwall, where one or more may be seen standing about the rivers or the muddy estuaries almost any day. Heronries are most numerous in Somerset with a smaller population in Devon and Cornwall. The 1928 census listed 37 heronries in the province with an average of 14 nests, the average in Somerset then being 25 and in the more westerly counties, 10 only. The Cornish heronry at Duloe held 28 nests but according to Ryves no heronry with more than 17 nests is now known in Cornwall. The largest heronry in the area in 1928 was in Somerton Wood, south of Glastonbury, with 100 nests.

A majority of the peninsular heronries are estuarine: all the principal Cornish colonies come into this category, while over the entire area they tend to be more numerous along the south coast, which is indented with winding creeks, each associated with a heronry. Thus the Exe had the ancient colony at Powderham

Castle which, once 40 to 50 nests strong, became extinct in 1910, when the birds moved to Eastdon House, Starcross: twenty-two years later herons again nested at Powderham and there were 4 nests there in 1935. Perhaps one should regard several small heronries in an estuary as one scattered colony rather than several separate ones, as in the Fal estuary where the principal heronry is near Philleigh but smaller ones are close by in both the Fal and Helford estuaries.

(*S. Lewis, P. I. R. Maclaren, E. M. Nicholson, A. G. Parsons, W. B. Tucker, W. Walmesley White, V. C. Wynne-Edwards*).

English Channel

When the 1928 census was taken, two of the four largest heronries in England, Arne in Dorset with 112 nests and Aldershaw Wood at Beckley in Sussex with 103-109, were in this faunal province, which also embraces Wiltshire, Hampshire and the Isle of Wight. In spite of these two large colonies the average size of the heronries within the area was only 11.3 nests. Both these colonies have occupied previous sites, the one now at Beckley, said to have contained 400 nests in 1840, has changed its ground twice. At Branksea Island in Dorset a heronry consisting of some 50 nests in 1834 flourished until it was deserted about 1855. Apparently the birds moved to Arne, which had increased from two nests in 1854-55 to a large colony in 1876. In 1924 there were between 30 and 40 nests, in 1928 the heronry had grown to around 112 nests but by 1938 it had reverted to between 30 and 40 and the nesting trees were burnt down in 1942. Subsequently all suitable nesting trees were felled to make a military training ground, nevertheless in 1946 there were 10 pairs in some comparatively small trees.

Although no great river-system drains the region many small rivers meander to the Channel. The chalk streams have their heron habitués (where they are allowed) and the small heronries are mostly within foraging distance of one of the rivers. The largest heronries are situated within reach of the most promising feeding-places. The Arne colony is associated with Poole Harbour, the

D

Beckley colony with Rye Harbour and the East Sussex marshes, the Arun supports the 58 pairs from Parham, while the waters surrounding Portsmouth are convenient to the birds from Goodwood.

(*Rev. F. L. Blathwayt, E. M. Cawkell, G. des Forges, M. Portal*).

THAMES DRAINAGE AREA

This area is of particular interest as it contains not only the counties of Kent, Surrey, Essex, Hertford, Middlesex, Berkshire, Oxford and Buckingham but also the greatest city in the world; moreover the average size of its heronries (23.4) is greater than anywhere else in Britain. No other area supports so large a human population as Greater London, but no other urban area is so well endowed with parks, lakes, riverside meadows and gravel pits. In Inner London alone there are nearly 1,200 acres of gardens, parks and open waters. As many as 20 herons have been counted at a time on the riverside meadows of Hampton Court Park; the bird is a frequent visitor to Regent's Park, where a wild one once attempted to nest with a captive, later released, from one of the Zoo aviaries. Herons frequently visit the Long Water in Kensington Gardens, the Serpentine and even ornamental garden pools.

No heronry has existed in the Metropolis since the middle of the nineteenth century but two remain within a mile of the County of London boundary. A colony of about 50 pairs on an island in a Walthamstow reservoir is but a short distance from the main street. A colony in Sidmouth Plantation, Richmond Park, founded by a single pair about 1880, reached a peak of 49 occupied nests in 1937, but declined by 1948 to 11 pairs. According to *The London Bird Report for 1948* there were 138 occupied herons' nests within "the suburbs and the fringe of open country still left within a circle of 20 miles' radius from St. Paul's Cathedral." Within this circle Kempton Park in Middlesex had 57 occupied nests in 1948, compared with 43 in 1945. This increase coincides with the decrease at Richmond Park, attributed to the operation of an A.A. battery in the immediate vicinity of the heronry.

According to the 1928 census the largest colony in the Thames

Drainage area was at St. Osyth, Essex, with 75 nests. The heronry at Chilham in Kent contained 57 nests; and, in existence since 1293, is the oldest known heronry in Britain.

(*W. B. Alexander, W. E. Glegg, N. F. Ticehurst, Members of the Essex Bird Watching Society, the London Natural History Society and Slough Natural History Society*).

OUSE DRAINAGE AREA

Very little of this faunal province, covering the counties of Norfolk, Suffolk, Cambridge, Bedford, Huntingdon and Northampton, lies over 300 feet above sea-level. The rivers, generally long with little fall, meander eastwards to the sea. The fens, except for a few fragments, have been reclaimed and the Broads are diminishing. Perhaps in the past there were even more herons in East Anglia than today but there are no reliable figures; the province now contains more herons' nests than any other part of Britain. In 1928 there were more nests known in Suffolk (188-97) than in 1884 (170). The changed biotic conditions appear to have reduced the average size of the heronries but the total number of herons remains about the same.

In some 40 heronries, including the Cambridgeshire sites, there are about 73 nests, the greatest number both of colonies and of nests in any region. The average size of colony, 19 nests, is exceeded in both the Thames and Mersey drainage areas but is higher than the average for England and Wales. The largest heronry in the whole of England and Wales, at Milton Park, Peterborough, contained 135 nests in 1928. This heronry, probably founded in 1819, occupies an inland site, but most of the larger heronries in East Anglia are adjacent to tidal waters and have mostly been in unbroken occupation. Generally the heronries are situated in the immediate vicinity of a river; in the eastern part of the province, away from the tidal reaches, they are smaller and have not been in so long or continuous occupation.

(*R. A. Hinde, K. Piercy, B. B. Rivière, Miss F. K. Staunton, C. F. Tebbutt, A. E. Vine*).

SEVERN DRAINAGE AREA

The presence of so many herons in late summer and autumn, taking advantage of temporary feeding places caused by flood waters and fishing in the rivers, gives an exaggerated impression of their numerical strength in this area. The source of the Severn in Plynlimmon Mountain is properly outside this faunal province. By Shrewsbury the river has gathered a considerable volume which varies greatly according to the pressure of its head-waters. With its tributary the Avon it is the natural drainage system for Shropshire, Stafford, Warwick, Worcester, Hereford, and Gloucester—a contrasting mixture of rural lands, industrial Birmingham and the Black Country. Below Gloucester it becomes tidal, receives the waters of the Wye at Monmouth and enters the Bristol Channel.

Throughout these counties there are 22 heronries, nearly as many as in the Thames province, although none in 1928 had more than 26 nests and the average size was only 11. Breeding herons do not abound in this area and probably never did, for most of the extinct heronries also were small. The two largest existing heronries, Warwick Park and Bagot's Park in Staffordshire, are both associated with the higher reaches where severe flooding is least likely to occur. Generally the easterly-flowing rivers are more stable and offer better feeding facilities than those which flow to the west and their estuaries frequently have a heronry. There is no Severn estuarine heronry and history has no record that there ever was one in the oak forests long ago cut down, although as many as 30 herons have been seen at one time on the mud left by the receding tide.

(*S. M. D. Alexander, H. A. Gilbert, H. E. Forrest, J. R. B. Masefield, C. A. Norris*).

TRENT DRAINAGE AREA

The 16 heronries in this province had in 1928-29 an average of 15 nests, with the largest colony at Willoughby Wood in Lincolnshire. The Trent follows its long winding course, mainly in a northerly direction, traversing the plain of Nottingham and

Lincolnshire, throughout the breadth of which it falls less than 300 feet. In these two counties the great majority of the heronries are situated; Leicestershire boasts but a single colony of 11 nests, in Derbyshire there is a single nest and in Rutland none.

It would be wrong to conclude from this present distribution that the absence of a breeding population in the Derbyshire dales is due to unsuitable conditions, for there was at one time a population of some 50 pairs based on 10 small heronries: tree-felling removed one site and trout-preservers extirpated the rest. The most spectacular loss in the Trent province is that of the heronry at Cressy Hall, Surfleet, where in 1792 Pennant claimed to have seen 80 nests in a single oak. Possibly fewer herons nest in this province than formerly because of the persecution in Derbyshire. Outside the nesting season, however, a heron is a familiar sight even in that forbidden land.

(*Rev. H. S. Allison, W. E. Mayes, G. R. Porter, J. S. Reeve, A. Roebuck*).

HUMBER DRAINAGE AREA

The vast county of Yorkshire is drained by the Humber and its tributaries. This gathering ground is for the most part a plain bounded on the west by the Pennines with the Yorkshire Moors and Wolds rising in the east. Perhaps in this more than in any other area the rivers are contaminated by industrial effluents, but the crystal clear dale-streams seem capable of supporting many more herons than nest in the area. Such good angling as these streams offer to the inhabitants of the nearby towns and cities has resulted in strict fish preservation, which certainly militates against heronries increasing.

At the present time there are some 12 heronries in the area with a rather low average of 10 nests apiece; the largest colony, at Hornsea Mere, had 21 nests in 1928. As 30 extinct heronries of varying size were listed in the census of 1928 it appears that many more herons bred in the Humber system a generation ago. There is no estuarine colony.

(*R. Chislett, Riley Fortune*).

MERSEY DRAINAGE AREA

This area, comprising the counties of Cheshire and Lancashire south of Lancaster, contains a large industrial tract with a vast human population and the plains of South Lancashire and Cheshire where agriculture and dairy farming are intensively practised. Here herons are surprisingly numerous. Occasionally they are to be seen flying over large towns and even over the centre of Manchester, while within a few miles of that city, at Worsley, a single pair sometimes nests. On the flashes, the result of mining subsidences on the South Lancashire coal-field, herons gather in strength; 25 have been counted on a summer day on the fields by Astley flash, their wings expanded in the sun. At Pennington flash, near Leigh, up to a dozen at a time could be seen until tipping of the town waste reduced both the area and attractiveness of the water. Wherever there is a pond on the coal-field offering food a heron may turn up; on some of the water-works reservoirs it is not unusual to find half-a-dozen herons feeding. In Cheshire the meres are the main feeding and breeding places.

The 8 heronries listed in the 1928 census do not include the solitary nest at Worsley. They had the large average of 21 nests, second only to that of the Thames area. The largest heronry at Eaton Hall, Chester, had 60 nests which in 1889 were nearly all in willows, but 30 years later most had been transferred to oaks. The reason for movements from one kind of tree to another is obscure; the explanation that the birds forsake a dying tree is not tenable, for there are numerous instances of herons having nested in dead trees, nor do they always realise that a tree has become unsafe, for I have seen many crashed nests and A. W. Boyd saw one at Tabley where both the adult and young were killed. (*A. W. Boyd*).

TYNE DRAINAGE AREA

A large portion of this province is above 600 feet. In the Cheviots and the Pennines the hills rise to 2,000 feet and more while much of the coastal belt is highly industrialised. It is not surprising therefore that the heron population is lower than in any other faunal province. In 1928, one small colony was recorded in Co. Durham and there were eight in Northumberland; in these nine heronries the average was 7 nests, as in Wales: the largest colony was Keilder with 11 nests. Most of the extinct heronries in the area were also very small, with the notable exception of Chillingham, which up to 1910 contained from 60 to 100 pairs. This fine heronry had existed from time immemorial until destroyed by tree-felling in the First World War; in 1928 it was represented by a single nest. In 1950 I found another single nest in Moralee Wood, Allanbanks, which does not appear to have been recorded, although I was told that a pair of herons had nested there for many years.

(*M. E. A. Davies, M. Portal, G. W. Temperley*).

ENGLISH LAKES AND THE ISLE OF MAN

Throughout the lakes, valleys and estuaries of Cumberland, Westmorland and North Lancashire the heron is common. Most widely distributed in autumn and winter, when odd birds may be encountered by streams in the highest hills, they tend to gather into small flocks on the salt-marshes and about the sandbanks, where they may be seen even in the breeding season.

The 27 heronries in the table are computed from the 1928-29 census, which listed 18 in Cumberland, 3 in Westmorland and 3 in North Lancashire, with the addition of 3 in the Isle of Man, where apparently none nested in 1928. The average size of the heronries, 9-10 nests, is probably a good deal less than half-a-century ago, although it is unlikely that the aggregate of nesting herons is much different. Tree-felling, intensified during two world wars, has worked against the continuation of large colonies and caused a dispersal of nesting sites. The largest heronry in Cumberland in 1928, that of Crofton, had 14 nests; the estate has since been taken over by the Land Settlement Scheme and very few herons remain. The oldest heronry in Cumberland existed before 1621, at Muncaster Castle, and is still maintained with about 5 nests.

The Dallam Tower heronry had 29 nests in 1928 and about 45 in 1940, the increase apparently being due to detachments of birds from Holker Moss and Rusland Moss, as the decline of these North Lancashire colonies coincided with the increase at Dallam. The heronry at Hamilton Wood, Lancaster, is of particular interest as it is said to have been started by deliberate transplantation of birds during the first decade of the nineteenth century. The Duke of Hamilton brought some herons from Hamilton Palace in Scotland, and kept them confined in the paddocks of Ashton Hall, Lancaster. Descendants of these birds founded and maintained the heronry at Crane Wood for almost a hundred years, before removing in their entirety to Hamilton Wood, where their successors still nest.

The Isle of Man contains a small but now constant resident population based on three heronries: in 1422 the Deemsters made a law imposing a penalty on anyone taking " hyrons," their young or eggs. At the end of the seventeenth century Sacheverell considered that there were too many "herns" on the island, but at the beginning of this century, although herons were numerous, Ralfe could not state with certainty that any then nested on Man, although he admitted the possibility of an odd pair or small colony in some remote spot. It is significant that while heronries of the Mersey province suffered a loss of almost 60 per cent of their populations in the following severe winter, the Manx populations were almost doubled.

(*E. Blezard, R. H. Brown, W. S. Cowin, L. E. Hope, W. F. Davidson*).

WALES

With three-quarters of the Principality 600 feet or more above sea-level the heronries tend to be crowded into such lowlands as are contained in the broader valleys, the coastal belt, especially where peninsular, and Anglesey. Herons based in the valleys of Wales are more limited as to their feeding grounds than the populations of most English colonies. These restricted valleys produce ribbon settlements of which the average size is lower than where there is freer foraging.

SOUTH WALES

In the counties of Glamorgan, Brecon, Radnor, Carmarthen, Pembroke and Cardigan 170 nests in 24 heronries gave an average of only 7 nests per colony. The largest, at Llanmiloe near Pendine in Carmarthen, with 20 nests is within reach of the estuaries of the Taff and Towy and not subject to any topographical foraging restrictions. The majority of the heronries are in river valleys, although the Vale of Glamorgan and Gower each have small ones, while amongst other small colonies in Pembrokeshire one or two are estuarine, being situated on Milford Haven. The Usk has a veritable chain of these small heronries but many other of the rivers have at least one based on them.

(*D. K. Bryson, H. E. Forrest, Kennedy Orton, J. D. R. Vernon, R. F. C. Zamboni*).

NORTH WALES

The northern counties of Wales are even more ruggedly mountainous than those of the south. In Montgomery, Merioneth, Carnarvon, Denbigh, Flint and Anglesey there are 15 heronries with an average of 7 nests. The largest at Tan-y-gaer, St. Asaph in Denbigh, is based on the Clwyd in a wide fertile valley. The Conway has no comparable heronry but several small colonies exist on both sides of the Menai Strait; and three or four others exist on the southern side of the Carnarvon peninsula. Although herons are often seen feeding in the mountain lakes and the estuaries which empty into Cardigan Bay in no case is a large heronry associated with these localities.

(*G. C. S. Ingram, Sir C. Dillwyn-Venables-Llewelyn, Bart.*).

SCOTLAND

A. Boyd Watt published in 1908 a list of 230 Scottish heronries, but precise modern figures are not available. Of Watt's 230 sites many were occupied by no more than a pair or two, while 45 were stated to be untenanted. It is probable that the number of Scottish breeding sites at the present time approximates to that of England and Wales, i.e. about 260. This must signify a greater concentration, for not only is the area of Scotland less than half the combined area of England and Wales, but also a considerable portion of Scotland, above the 1,000 foot contour, is outside the heron's normal breeding terrain in these islands.

The species is resident in every Scottish mainland county, but none of the heronries approach their English counterparts in size. The population is densest in the Border Counties, in the south-west, through Ayrshire, about the Clyde estuary and surrounding islands, and in the north-west Highlands and Islands. Herons are numerous in Inverness-shire, Aberdeenshire and about the Tay but much fewer in the Central Highlands and along the industrial belt from the Forth to the Clyde.

An apparent increase in the winter population noticed in many places, as in Sutherland, may be the result of local movement, the birds which haunt the burns going down towards the sea when the weather closes in. There is no doubt that the resident population of Wigtown is augmented in winter from the north and east; its seaboard, with Loch Ryan and Luce Bay which almost sequesters Galloway and a climate capable of supporting a sub-tropical vegetation, provides an ideal wintering ground. The short sea passage from Galloway to the even kindlier climes of Antrim and Down make Wigtown a point of concentration for birds either wintering there or on passage to Ireland.

A few herons breed in Orkney, while larger numbers winter there: the heron is an occasional visitor to the Fair Isle and passes through regularly on migration; in Shetland it occurs every month of the year but the slight evidence of former nesting, mentioned by Saxby, has never been authenticated. Small numbers are resident in the Inner and Outer Hebrides, winter visitors swelling the populations; and occasionally, in summer, a heron has crossed to St. Kilda.

(*Miss E. V. Baxter, Miss L. J. Rintoul, A. Watson*).

IRELAND

Although Ussher and Warren published an extensive list of Irish heronries in 1900, this was by no means a complete survey of the Irish populations. The nests are so scattered and observers so few that an accurate census seems impossible at present. What is known, however, reveals the presence of the heron throughout Ireland with breeding colonies in every county and an additional winter influx.

I am indebted to R. F. Ruttledge and C. D. Deane for information concerning the heron's present status in the Republic and Ulster respectively. During the last half-century there has been no noticeable change in the number of herons, although there has been a considerable redistribution, resulting in a reduction of the size of the colonies and an increase in the occurrence of odd nests. Ussher in his *Birds of Ireland* considered colonies of over 20 nests as large and did not cite any with as many as 50. Many of the larger heronries are now extinct and Ruttledge does not know of any with more than 25 nests, while the average appears to be about 8 nests. The reasons for this redistribution are obvious; the breaking up of many large estates and, more recently, wholesale felling of hardwood trees, have speeded the process of disintegration. The heron has now adapted itself to the expedient of breeding in out-of-the-way places, so that very often a solitary nest, or small groups of two or three are found, and a veritable army of observers would be required to make a count.

It is sometimes difficult even to define the boundaries of an Irish heronry, as for example when a string of islands in a lough are each occupied by one or two pairs. On L. Carra, in Mayo, a water some 6 by 1½ miles, there are about five islands so occupied. From year to year the population of the several islands fluctuates, apparently due to interchange, and it is questionable whether these birds should be regarded as five separate heronries or as a single unusually scattered one.

CONCLUSION

The foregoing survey indicates that in 1928 only four of the heronries in England and Wales contained 100 occupied nests. The largest, at Milton Park, Peterborough, numbered 135; the one at Arne in Dorset, now felled, reached 112; the Sussex heronry

at Aldershaw, which in 1939 started to move to Rye and Win-
chelsea, contained 109; while Somerton Wood in Somerset held
100. Inclusive of those named, there were 8 with upwards of 70,
8 with 50-70, 16 with 30-50, 22 with 20-30, 64 with 10-20,
63 with 5-10 and 74 with 1-5 occupied nests. The average size
of all the heronries included in the count was 15 nests; the most
populous British colony was only a tenth the size of the largest
Dutch one at the same period; in not more than ten British
heronries was the number of nests greater than the number sometimes accommodated in one tree in Asia.

New nests may be built while old ones are untenanted. This
partly accounts for the fact that there are generally more nests
than breeding pairs in any sizeable heronry. In 1946 R. L. Brown
sent me figures concerning three Scottish heronries. At Kelbourne
there were about 50 nests, at Roseneath 40 and at Lake of Men-
teith 70, yet none of these colonies held more than 15 pairs of
breeding herons in any recent season. Knabe made similar observations in 9 East Prussian heronries from 1931 to 1936 and
found no constant ratio from heronry to heronry or from year to
year: the lowest percentage of vacant nests was 5, the highest 35.

From these censuses it is apparent that heron populations
fluctuate. W. B. Alexander now summarises the annual sample
count, organised by the British Trust of Ornithology and publishes
the results as *The Index of Heron Population* in the magazine *British
Birds*. By taking the census return for 1928 as 100 comparative
figures can be deduced, showing any increase or decrease in the
breeding stock. The "index" figure of 100 denotes a population
level towards which the breeding stock tends to recover after a
set-back. The years 1928, 1936, 1937, 1938 and 1939 had an index
of 100 and it is convenient to refer to them as normal in taking a
long-term view of the fluctuations. In fourteen of the years for which
records are available, ten of which are in sequence, the populations
did not vary by more than + 5 or — 8 per cent. The lowest figure
was a decrease of 40 per cent in 1947, following an exceptionally
long frost. During the period, the normal (index 100) breeding
population of England and Wales was 3,800 pairs, with a maximum of 3,990 and a minimum of 2,280 pairs.

Apart from general fluctuations it is well established that one or several heronries in an area may sometimes suffer a sudden decline. When this occurs there is often a corresponding increase in the colonies of an adjoining area. The upper limit of a heronry's population is set by the birds' food requirements and by available nesting space; but when a colony grows much faster than could be accounted for by its own potential natural increase, this must be due only to a movement of population. I have already cited the history of Dallam Tower as an instance and others will come readily to mind. Any map of heronries may be suddenly outdated by these movements.

In Britain the two main factors responsible for a decline in heron populations are exceptionally severe winters and man, the heron's only active enemy. Here the birds do not escape the rigours of winter by migration, as on the continent, and, though they wander, many die of starvation in prolonged periods of frost. A decrease in the number of breeding pairs, as Alexander has shown, is largely the result of the prevailing lowest temperature of the preceding winter, and as a rather high percentage of the victims are young birds, the effect on the heronries is noticeable for two following seasons.

Such years as 1917, 1928, 1940 and 1947 were disastrous for the heron, and from the *Index of Heron Population* it can be estimated that in 1928 Britain had 600 fewer pairs of breeding herons than in the previous year. In 1940 an even greater loss was found to have taken place, 1,000 pairs apparently having perished. The graphs compiled by W. B. Alexander, which correlate the residual breeding population with the mean temperature of the coldest month of the preceding winter, supply conclusive evidence that severe weather is, in this country, the greatest factor controlling the heron population.

There is no doubt that many young birds, less wary than the adults, are shot in Britain. Recovery figures may be misleading, for although the majority of shot ringed birds are probably reported, many which have met their end from some other cause are never found, so that the figure for shot birds is probably too high a percentage of the total loss. The greatest slaughter takes

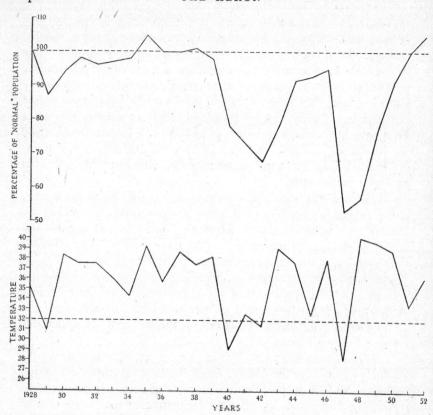

FIG. 4

Residual breeding population compared with the mean temperature of the
coldest month of the preceding winter (after W. B. Alexander)

place in the trout angling counties. In most heronries the birds
are protected by the owners and in many counties enjoy a nominal
legal protection but they are such great wanderers that legal
protection within county limits affords little real security.

In the past the worst accounts of shooting came from Ireland.
According to Ussher and Warren the tenant of a fishery in Connemara and his hirelings destroyed 90 herons in one day; the same

authors record the destruction of 500 to 600 herons' eggs in one season. It is surprising that herons are so numerous in Ireland in view of such mass destruction as took place just before 1900; but modern Irish anglers are less vindictive. In parts of Scotland to this day the slaughter is great, but fish-hatchery owners cannot be blamed for protecting their property. The same applies to the carp-pond proprietors in Europe. But there is no justification for indiscriminate shooting. Reports of damage to fisheries are usually exaggerated and take account of only one part of the heron's commissariat. The record of destruction by shooting in Germany is far worse than in Britain. The personal life-bag of the last Kaiser included 826 cormorants and herons, while more recently an examination of the ringed bird recoveries in the various states revealed wholesale destruction; in Brandenburg 66 per cent mortality through human agency; in Grenzmark-West Prussia 75 per cent; in Schleswig-Holstein 75 per cent. Young birds were shot from under the nests, as young rooks are shot in this country.

There is no known epidemic disease affecting herons, but a comparatively insignificant number perish from a variety of accidents. Death by choking with large prey is not uncommon. There are cases of herons having been killed in collision with various obstacles, high tension cables, barbed wire and the like. I heard of an alleged case in Northumberland where water froze round a heron's legs and held it captive in the same way that, in some northern zoos, flamingos have been known to get frozen up. In Germany a heron died through becoming entangled in algae while fishing. However these, and other cases of death by misadventure, have probably very little effect on the heronries.

As to the future status of the heron in Britain we can but speculate. There is, however, an optimum size to any population, whether of a region, a country or a colony, beyond which the community may not successfully extend. On the other hand denuded colonies have strong recuperative powers and the *Index of Heron Population* shows that a stricken heronry is usually quick to recover its optimum strength.

I have reviewed the reasons why heronries flourish or decline and considered the hazards the bird has to meet. We have seen the heronry regarded almost as an object of veneration in the old game laws, and we have seen it destroyed as the abode of vermin. Today the heron generally occupies a favoured position, but many jaundiced eyes still follow its flight to the waterside, and heronries may suffer through the preservation of fishing interests. At the once-flourishing colony at Herringfleet, in Suffolk, " all the young ones were killed by one of the keepers to furnish maggots for their pheasants " (c. 1865). The pheasant has indeed ousted the heron in popularity, for while we read in L'Estrange's Accounts of an " Item paid at Lynn when we went hawking to Wolferton Wood for Fyer and Drinke," the *Nationalist* for 1853 informs us that in the same wood " the keepers were destroying the herons as their noise disturbed their game." More recently a heronry was destroyed because the birds' noise disturbed the meditations of the religious body into whose possession it had passed ! Yet the population is well maintained and if there seem to be fewer herons in Britain now than in Gilbert White's day it may be because records are more exact and exactitude tends to minimise. Certainly over a long period the species appears to have been fairly static and unless there is a major change of opinion against it, a vast tree-felling campaign, or a succession of abnormal winters, there is no reason apparent why its numerical strength should not remain within its present limits.

CHAPTER 5

FOOD AND FORAGING

To ILLUSTRATE how catholic are the heron's tastes I give two incidents concerning captive birds. A semi-tame heron seized and swallowed a Persian kitten. Another, which fell from a nest in Germany, was kept captive and fed on veal and pork until it escaped.

Because it is partially a fish-eater the heron has been persecuted far beyond its deserts, for it is virtually omnivorous and its feeding habits vary with prevailing conditions. An angler seeing a heron catch a trout is immediately biased against it; he does not see the eels beneath the nesting trees nor does he examine the pellets. In considering the nature of the heron's food I have drawn upon all available information and, to the tangible results of stomach-content examination, analysis of pellets and regurgitated matter, I have added many observations made from close watching. Only by correlating the results obtained from all these methods is it possible to assess properly the heron's diet.

In all the herons I have found dead, both the stomach and gullet have been empty. Either the bird had regurgitated—which it is always very ready to do—or everything had been digested before death. I have had no birds shot but other observers have examined the contents of the digestive tract in a number of instances. In Germany 21, 17 and 14 mice were found in the stomachs of three herons. F. W. Frohawk found nothing but prawns in the stomach of another, while various people have reported credible or incredible numbers or weights of fish taken from the stomachs of shot herons. I shall consider some of these cases in greater detail when discussing the amount of food taken.

Birds of many kinds rid themselves of the indigestible parts of

E

their food by regurgitating it in the form of pellets. Pellet analysis provides a convenient means of finding out what a bird has eaten: but in the case of the heron a quite erroneous conclusion would result from this method alone. It is possible to collect pellets below the nests and throughout 1948 I picked up over 100 at Scarisbrick, 2 of which are depicted in plate 2d, p. 3. A. Hibbert-Ware classified heron pellets in five forms, viz., fur pellets of a regular, irregular, or modular type, feather pellets, and plant pellets. The almost complete absence of fish remains is surprising until one realises that fish-bones are reduced to a liquid state by the bird's digestive juices, while to some extent mammalian and avian bones resist their action. Although it is impossible therefore to assess the heron's diet from pellet data alone they are a means of identifying items other than fish. Newly ejected pellets are so strongly acid as to turn a blue litmus paper red. When mammal or bird bones occur they are usually pitted like pumice-stone, and the bone is finally reduced to a particle-size no greater than coarse sand. Claws and teeth are the last parts to remain intact, the enamel of teeth often alone remaining.

Thirty-two Dam Wood pellets were weighed (after being dried at room temperature) and measured over their greatest dimension. Any pieces of twig projecting beyond the contour of the solid pellet were included in the measurements which, together with their weights and contents, are listed at the end of this chapter. It will be noted from this table that size bears little relationship to weight, as the density of the pellets varies enormously.

In 1912 L. Florence found that 10 of the 23 pellets she examined contained vegetable matter, yet Collinge, in his analysis of the stomach contents of five herons, found only 1.5 per cent of such material in the form of seed fragments and the stems of aquatic plants. A. Hibbert-Ware found considerable amounts of vegetable matter in her examination of pellets and I have found such material as macerated wood-fibre, grasses, chaff and pieces of twig up to 10-cm. in length. The presence of so much vegetable substance, much more than could have been eaten by accident or contained in other food, points to the conclusion that the heron eats it for some purpose. Several times in 1948 and 1949 I saw

adult birds regurgitate masses of vegetable matter into the nest for
their brood to eat and I have, too, watched young herons eating
pieces of their nests. While it is possible that some of this vegetable
material supplies vitamins, herons eat twigs from their nests, in
the absence of other matter, for roughage, to be agglutinated in
pellet formation; when the diet is mainly of fish more vegetation
is eaten. Once I saw a young heron, after a meal of fish, swallow
a pellet which had been previously regurgitated and crushed;
this, like the vegetable matter, was probably taken as a digestive
accessory, to aid pellet-formation.

There were no recognisable batrachian remains in any of the
pellets I dissected although herons eat quantities of both newts and
frogs. I saw a heron frog-hunting alongside a little owl at a
spawning pond in early spring and A. G. Parsons saw one probing
for frogs in the muddy bed of a Yorkshire stream one March, when
snow was lying six inches deep. The tenant of some west country
osier-beds suspected that the dismembered bodies of frogs and
toads he found there had been mutilated by herons, but I do not
believe they kill them except for food.

In 1789 the Abbé Spallanzani found that tin tubes containing
a fish and a frog, inserted in a heron's stomach, were merely dinted
although the creatures contained therein were completely digested.
In the same experiment made on fowls the tubes were remarkably
twisted by the birds' powerful gizzards. From these experiments
there seems no doubt that it is the reaction of the acid digestive
secretions rather than any mechanical disintegration, which
accounts for the almost complete absence of fish remains in pellets.
A further curious action of these juices was first noticed by C. B.
Ticehurst, who remarked that prawns he took from a dead heron
had turned pink. Later F. W. Frohawk found no fewer than 84
common prawns (*Leander serratus*) in the gullet and stomach of a
heron, all of which had turned bright pink.

The Dam Wood pellets show to what a great extent mammals
are eaten by herons. In this series water-voles predominate and
the presence of a heronry must have a large bearing upon the local
vole population. The pellets which A. Hibbert-Ware analysed
were procured from Cambridgeshire, Essex, Norfolk, Sussex and

Carmarthen; some from every source, and collectively over 55 per cent contained mole fur. There were 150 with moles to 24 with brown rats. Because of a rat infestation near one of the Essex heronries, the remains of these rodents here exceeded those of water-voles; except for this case water-voles were second in frequency to moles. Of the pellets taken from roosting sites in Surrey during every month of the year, more than 80 per cent were composed of mole-fur. From such a series it might appear that these herons had fed on little else save voles and moles: but this is far from the truth. It is remarkable that the mole should enter into a heron's diet at all. An occasional one might be taken on the surface when going to drink; but the presence of so many suggests that the birds have found a way of taking them from their tunnels. I have often seen herons standing on the mole-infested sandy soil flanking Morecambe Bay and, although I have never actually seen one catch a mole in its tunnel, I have little doubt that it is able to detect its presence.

The process of regurgitation, though providing a convenient means of ejecting indigestible parts in the form of pellets, sometimes involves a considerable wastage of food. The main stimuli to regurgitation are fear and the begging of the young. Juvenile gulls handled when "freezing" often throw up food on being released; adult gulls empty their gullets when chased by skuas. Fright is the reason for this; and it was fright which caused a brood of young herons in Dam Wood to throw up two eighteen-inch-long eels and a water-vole. Once when climbing to a nest I found my neck encircled by a partly digested eel; at the top of the tree four young herons, with necks outstretched over the nest-rim, were all being violently "sick." In America C. M. Kirkpatrick, by stone-throwing and rapping the nesting trees, induced a colony of young great blue herons (*Ardea h. herodias*) to regurgitate 297 specimens, which enabled him to assess their diet.

In Britain, herons have never been systematically frightened to make them regurgitate, although dropped food is often found beneath the nesting trees. The fish recorded are trout, eels, chub, roach, rudd, perch, pike, carp, lamprey, minnow, stickleback, miller's thumb, samlet and grayling. Eels have been my most frequent finds at Dam Wood, followed by perch, roach and chub. Flounders are taken in some districts, quite a fair number being carried to the heronries in northern Lancashire.

Occasionally skeletons are found beneath the trees. In my possession is a perfect chub skeleton measuring twelve inches, which was picked up in Montgomeryshire; other fish skeletons up to fourteen inches long have been found. There is no doubt that these are skeletons of fish disgorged by herons before digestion had affected the bones. Beneath nests I have also found, sometimes reduced to skeletons, water-voles, mice and water-shrews.

Useful as is the study of these remains, it is also necessary to watch the heron actually foraging and eating, which also discloses the means by which the prey is caught.

The heron's method of dealing with frogs and moles has already been described. I have seen herons rat-catching round an old dung-hill near Dam Wood. Their method was to watch and wait, and the pellets proved considerable success. A captive was killed by a few sharp blows then swallowed whole and dry. Normally bodies are dipped in water before swallowing, but an account of another dry meal is recorded in which the heron had played with a rat, cat-and-mouse fashion, until dead. It was swallowed head first, and to judge by the bird's contortions and the length of time taken to swallow the hindmost parts—the process took at least ten minutes—the absence of water as a lubricant occasions considerable difficulties.

T. A. Coward saw five rats swallowed in succession, each being first dipped in water. Tame herons in my care carried small pieces of horse-flesh a considerable distance to moisten before eating them. Although the herons at Scarisbrick caught rats in the manner described, they will also search them out. Twenty-four herons walking line abreast over a newly-cut oat-field were probably rodent hunting, as was another party seen one November day at Forteviot, by the river Earn. In Berwickshire they have been known to hunt pheasant ground for rats and when no more were to be had they turned their attention to the rats in a sheep-yard.

Field-voles (*Microtus*) are taken at all times of the year. Herons shot during severe winters on the marshy ground near Southport have had very little other than field-voles in their stomachs. Field-mice (*Apodemus sylvaticum*), too, are captured. I have a note concerning a visit to an Essex heronry in March when pellets composed of rodent remains were found and a dead mouse lay on a branch below one of the nests. These small rodents enter into a heron's diet to a considerable extent in this country and perhaps even more so in Germany.

Water-voles (*Arvicola amphibius*), and probably water-shrews (*Neomys fodiens*) (whose remains have been found in pellets) are sometimes caught while swimming. Herons are quite accomplished if infrequent swimmers, and I have a note of one catching a water-vole by swimming after it. The number of water-voles taken to Dam Wood far exceeded the total of all other rodents. Indeed, judging from the evidence of pellets alone, one would conclude that these animals form the heron's staple diet. They were caught as they left their holes. I have never found one in the debris below the nests which had been pierced by its captor's bill. Herons deal with mammals as with fish, either dispatching them by direct blows from the beak, or by battering them against a convenient anvil.

Two instances of herons taking weasels are recorded by Eric Parker. In the first a bird in Northumberland had a full-grown weasel in its gullet and in the second a heron was seen to catch, kill and eat a weasel by a sea-wall near Colchester: it was taken to the water and dipped before being swallowed. Numbers of heron pellets were found containing the skulls of "both weasels and stoats."

We have seen that on occasion one young heron may make a meal of another, alive or dead, and the remains of adult dabchicks, snipe, wood-pigeon, robin, blackbird, starling and sparrow have been found in the pellets and stomachs of herons. The young of mallard, moorhen and other waterfowl are picked up whenever opportunity offers. A heron once picked up a cockerel but straight-way dropped it, and once some poultry feathers were found in a pellet; that is all the evidence I can find that the bird has a taste for domestic poultry.

Adult moorhens occasionally provide a meal for a heron, but

they are too large to be swallowed easily and not infrequently choke their captor; the curator of a provincial museum has had three herons brought to him choked in this way. It has been recorded that some herons fed on exhausted snipe during a period of keen frosts, when their usual foraging ground was ice-bound.

There are records of herons having taken tern chicks, and on Priest Island, in Wester Ross, Fraser Darling noticed that they habitually preyed upon the downy chicks of lesser blackbacks and herring-gulls.

There are very few definite records of herons eating reptiles in this country, though remains of slow-worm, grass-snake and adder have been found in pellets. Probably the grass-snakes have been caught while swimming and as even adders are known to take to water, it may be that herons take adders when visiting moorland streams. In this country, however, the taking of reptiles must be regarded as exceptional. Grass-snakes have been mentioned as among the food of the heron in Italy, while in Africa the birds are said to spend much time hunting lizards far from water.

Invertebrates form a considerable part of a heron's diet. In nearly half the sample of pellets from Dam Wood were remains of pond-beetles. The large species *Dytiscus marginalis* is taken in great numbers and smaller beetles also occur. Other aquatic insects regularly taken include water-scorpions and the larvae of dragon-flies. Sometimes freshwater-mussels are taken—I have seen shells emptied by the herons about the banks of a water in Cheshire. In parts of Somerset herons have often been seen to take mussels up a high river-bank to break them open on dry land, where hundreds of the broken shells lay about. A. Hibbert-Ware found fragments of grasshoppers in several of the pellets she examined and these insects are probably preyed upon in Britain to a much greater extent than is suspected; in Africa herons eat many grasshoppers. Other small creatures, such as earwigs and woodlice, which may have been eaten by the heron, or been contained in some larger prey, have been found in pellets. So far as I can ascertain grasshoppers are the only terrestrial invertebrates habitually eaten.

Many herons stay away from fresh water for long periods, and may be seen picking over the flotsam by marine rock-pools, catching unconsidered trifles on tide-exposed sandbanks, or working in estuaries. Many which haunt the marine loughs of Ireland, or the wilder Scottish coasts, subsist entirely on marine fauna for a considerable part of the year and I have often surprised them working through the seaweed and pools for shore-crabs, prawns, flatfish or whatever else the tide had left. A. Blake-Knox said they ate starfish, but I have no other confirmation of that; he said, too, that herons came " like Virgil's harpies to the obscene feast left by fishermen after baiting their hooks for long-line fishing, taking besides sea-anemones and starfish the entrails and trimmings of skate." I have known them take hermit-crabs thrown out by Scottish fishermen when extracting whelks for bait. In Germany they have shown a taste for the mitten-crab (*Eriocheir sinensis*), a freshwater crab indigenous to China, which now infests European rivers from Flanders to Finland.

Knowledge of the food so far discussed is based upon the tangible evidence of remains which throw a disproportionate emphasis on animals other than fish, yet it is as a fish-hunter that the heron is most familiar, as it stands statue-like in shallow water or slowly wades in search of prey. Vertical stance enables it to face the sun irrespective of the wind direction, and thus avoid disarranging its feathers or casting a shadow on the water. The heron is only able to fish in this way where it can approach by wading from dry land down a gently sloping incline to a depth not exceeding about a foot.

Once I saw a heron, fishing in the shallows by a Thames weir, make a lightning grab to catch a chub. It walked to the top of the bank where it put down the fish, which several times jumped towards the river and as often was retrieved: having killed it the bird found it too big to swallow and flew off. A heron rose from a Sussex stream carrying a ten-inch trout; on being startled, however, it dropped the fish which the observer returned to the water apparently uninjured. Yet another bird was seen to carry ashore a large carp which it killed by a series of blows; before each blow the heron retreated a few paces, flexed itself, crouching slightly, then darted forward to the attack and between blows the victim was carried to the water and dipped. When it was dead the heron swallowed it, with its bill submerged during most of the operation and its neck greatly distended.

A heron kills its prey before eating it by every variety of ill-treatment; only once have I heard of a fish being eaten alive—an eel which was later disgorged still living, but with part of its skin damaged by the bird's digestive processes. There is a popular supposition that the heron catches and kills its prey by stabbing, but my experience does not bear this out, for I have never seen any victim bearing a wound consistent with this method of capture.

Herons do not always stand patiently waiting for victims to come within reach but often go in search of them. Both methods are practicable only in the shallows; but while waiting the bird relies on assimilation with its surroundings, rather than on stealth. In contrast to the deliberation shown by the waiting heron are the hasty movements sometimes made by the bird seeking out its prey. I once saw one, after vainly waiting, break into a skipping gait with wings unfolded to maintain its balance and arrive at a fresh place to try its skill. There it regained its poise and, wrapped in its grey mantle, concentrated upon the shallows.

Although the heron does so much foraging in water up to a depth of twelve inches a good deal of evidence has accumulated to show how the barrier of greater depth is overcome. Where the water is too deep for wading it will hunt by swimming after or diving upon its prey.

I believe all birds can swim and it is not surprising therefore that herons, although not habitual swimmers, will do so when necessity demands. On occasions there is no apparent reason for their swimming, but the presence of food in deep water is usually the incentive. One instance brought to my notice was of a heron swimming straight up to a moorhen's nest and devouring the young, and I once watched one swimming on a Lancashire "flash," around which several others were fishing in orthodox fashion. Bolam recorded a case of a heron fishing near a crowd of gulls and divers a quarter-of-a-mile out to sea from Aberystwyth; after trying once to get a fish it rose easily from the water and returned to the rocks. When taking to deep water herons usually fly straight down and settle on the surface, swimming with ease and riding high. At Combermere in Cheshire I saw a heron wade out of its depth until it was swimming; later it rose from the water as easily as a gull. M. T. Hill has described an incident of three herons walking out of their depth and swimming about for a time before returning to wade; J. Sneyd Taylor records a further instance of this at Van Ryneveld's Pass irrigation lake in South Africa. All recorders of swimming herons, save one, are agreed that the birds ride high in the water, the exception being Blake-Knox who alleged that he saw herons lying in the water at Wexford with only their heads and necks above the surface.

There is ample evidence of the heron's diving prowess—by reliable witnesses from as far back as Newcombe, the last of the great heron-hawkers. Newcombe left a record of a heron plunging head-first into a marsh dyke five or six feet deep, and emerging with a two-pound pike. Recent observations have been made of herons diving from a steep river-bank, from a perch provided by an overhanging willow, and from a canal bank: it thus appears that they will either dive, or fly down to deep water. On a voyage from Amsterdam to Harderwijk, across the Zuider Zee, Fischer and Ladiges saw herons fishing after the manner of gulls. Flying from six to nine feet high and suddenly turning they would descend to within a foot or two of the surface, and maintaining their height by a tern-like fluttering, seize their prey, rise again and swallow it in the air. D. Grimeger later gave a corroborative account of this procedure, with the addition that the herons alighted on the water, leisurely closed their wings, picked up their prey and rose again. In a personal letter P. A. D. Hollom tells of a heron diving tern-like to a reservoir to collect a fish which floated on the top and may have been dead; in Cheshire A. W. Boyd has seen herons hovering before settling on Marbury Mere; while in Surrey P. I. R. Maclaren saw one catch a fish by diving from the air into a pond, and the Duke of Bedford saw another with gull-like flight pick up some prey from the Thames.

This gull-like method of fishing, which until recent years had escaped notice, is no mere local adaptation, for a particularly interesting example is described by J. Sneyd Taylor, who saw, during January, 1936, as many as five herons at once, flying slowly, almost hovering over and diving into the large irrigation dam at Graaf-Reinet in the Karroo. Working over deep water, they dropped straight in from a considerable height, head and feet first and sometimes came up with fish. From time to time the birds came ashore to rest or remained sitting on the surface between dives, later resuming their strange method of fishing. A strong wind was favourable to hovering, which however also took place in calm weather.

Once at the Ryneveld's Pass irrigation lake, pied kingfishers (*Ceryle rudis*) squabbling over their catches dropped them, and the herons standing nearby were quick to pick them up. An instance of opportunist behaviour is mentioned in N. H. Southern's account of the heronry at Buscot in Berkshire. He saw two herons, one flying a little ahead of the other and carrying a fish which it dropped into the lake; the second bird dived after the fish but failed to recover it and swam about for a spell before making off.

There is much speculation as to how much of the day and night the heron spends in foraging. Several consecutive springs I stayed in a Suffolk village. Behind the house was a dyke teeming with fish and nightly at dusk herons came to fish there: they fished at the edge of darkness, they were fishing at dawn and some remained throughout the night. When watching flighting duck in the Ribble estuary I have often seen herons in the tributaries and, on recrossing the marsh long after dark, I have disturbed them on the saltings. Stevenson wrote that in Norfolk he " started them one after the other from the water's edge with the earliest dawn of morning," but the statement of A. E. Knox that " so far from being relaxed after sunset " the parental duties of these birds " appear to be redoubled during the night " does not accord with my experience.

On the night of 16-17 April, 1949, 17 broods were in the nests at Scarisbrick. Greatly increased activity occurred from a little before sunset until half-an-hour after. During the next half-hour feeding was ascertained at four nests and other birds fed at 1 hour 45 minutes and 2 hours 35 minutes after sunset. But undoubtedly some of the adult birds spend the night away from the heronry and these may provide meals at dawn. I have disturbed herons at every hour of the day and night but, from the condition of the ground where they were flushed, I believe they had been roosting, not feeding.

While herons may feed their young during the hours of darkness the frequency is greatly reduced. In my opinion, reports of herons' nocturnal activities have been much exaggerated. They certainly forage late and early, and some habitually roost in the marshes when, if food comes their way, they will profit by it, but the reduced feeding activity in the heronries at night may be taken as an indication of the bird's feeding habits.

Herons may forage anywhere, but they show such strong attachment to certain places that these might be regarded as regular feeding grounds. Certain sandbanks in Morecambe Bay have attracted herons for as long as anyone can remember, and many an inland waterway has a heron habitually on it. E. A. Ellis tells me that on the Norfolk broads they approach the water so often by the same route that the reeds are broken down into regular pathways. In September, 1948, reaches of the river Wye, below Hereford, rose six feet, with the result that a shallow bay much frequented by herons was temporarily inaccessible; yet when I visited the place after the spate impressions of herons' feet were there at every level, showing that the birds had returned after the water had risen beyond wading depth. Other places may be temporarily favoured: open waters in time of drought sometimes attract all the herons in a district. Concentration may be seen when sea-trout and brown trout move up to their spawning beds. J. Hughes Parry has seen fifteen together at such times on a tributary of the Welsh Dee where normally there is never more than the odd heron.

Sometimes herons visit fish-farms where, naturally, they are not tolerated; I know of one hatchery in Scotland where many have been destroyed; they do not, however, descend on stew-ponds in the numbers that might be expected. I wished to examine all the shot herons I could, and approached several English fish-rearers, who all promised that I should have what they shot—but pointed out that, although they shoot any herons poaching about their establishments, this only happens occasionally. Any pond containing fish may attract herons; even goldfish are taken from little pools in London gardens. Usually herons are wary, fishing late and early, but occasionally they grow bold: a small pond in Somerset, well stocked with rudd, was visited each day by a heron that allowed dogs or men to approach quite close; it fished there until every rudd was taken, then transferred its attention to some goldfish ponds and was shot by the village postman. Yet many goldfish ponds remain for years unmolested. As a protection I would suggest running a series of wires across the shallows.

The quantity and size of fish herons take has been greatly exaggerated. The most extravagant description of a heron's voracity is probably the statement of Bishop Stanley—that inside a dead bird picked up in Scotland there were found " the extraordinary number of thirty-nine fine trout." If those trout had averaged only an ounce and a half their combined weight would have equalled that of their captor. A more credible account was given by the late Viscount Powerscourt who told me that, on opening a heron which had been shot on his little river, he found that it contained five quite nice-sized little trout—which would be a good meal, for twelve ounces of food daily suffices to keep a captive heron in health.

A two-pound pike has overtaxed the capacity of a heron's gullet and choked it, yet there are persistent reports of much heavier fish being killed and carried away. A keeper shot a heron which was flying with difficulty and took from it a sea-trout *estimated*, by him and by the head watcher of the Loch Lomond Angling Association, to weigh three pounds. A correspondent to the *Irish Times* (16 November, 1945) claimed knowledge of a heron having killed a four-pound grilse. I do not believe that a heron could lift such a weight, for H. A. Gilbert found that although a golden eagle could carry a blue hare of six or seven pounds with ease, it had great difficulty in rising with it; in ideal conditions birds of prey can just lift their own weight, but herons have no such exceptional lifting capacity.

It is interesting to survey the effects of the heron upon fish populations. First thoughts are usually of the bird as a destroyer, but a fuller appreciation of the facts may give a different impression. The destruction wrought by eels upon other fish is very heavy indeed; elvers swarm into our rivers in such prodigious numbers that they appear as a mass of wriggling forms, extending for many yards across half the width of the river. There they live for several years, thriving upon food that salmon and trout could have eaten and when they are part-grown they eat salmon-fry and parr, young sea-trout and young brown trout. Dame Juliana Berners wrote " the Ele is a quaysy Fysshe. A ravenour and devourer of the brode of Fysshe " and ever since eels have been accused of eating the spawn of salmon and trout. Although it is doubtful whether they actually eat many of the ova—indeed many have ceased feeding for the winter by the time the fish spawn—they burrow about in the " redds ", as the spawning scrapes are called, and uncover them and any that are uncovered are lost. P. D. Malloch considers the eel " by far the greatest enemy that salmon and trout have." As herons probably eat more eels than all other species of fish together, they may actually be beneficial to salmon and trout waters. Even where a concentration of herons has gathered at the sea-trout " redds," they have been seen to take eels in preference to trout.

Admittedly herons take trout, of which the majority are small since the larger they grow the safer they become. The two factors necessary to produce big trout are relatively warm water and abundant food; it is well known that a trout in a mountain stream may weigh no more in ounces than another of the same age in a well-provided river may weigh in pounds. It is useless to introduce large Loch Leven trout into a water swarming with little trout with a view to improving it, for the additional big trout will make a further drain on the already inadequate food-supply and the native fish will become even lighter. If half the undersized trout were netted out the remainder would have twice as much food and grow larger. If a heron thins out the numbers the effect is the same and it achieves a result which large sums of money spent on introducing trout has often failed to do. In many circumstances the heron should be regarded as an efficient control, rather than a pest.

To a charge, sometimes made against the heron, that its bill may introduce furunculosis into a healthy water, the facts are a complete answer. Furunculosis in fish is, like so many disease germs in human beings, probably always present. It develops only in sick fish.

Summary and Conclusions

The heron feeds on all manner of aquatic and terrestrial animals. Fish, frogs, beetles, moles, water-voles and rats are among the commonest prey. I have called it omnivorous because it swallows much vegetable matter, from which it derives no nourishment, but which it needs for pellet-formation.

Catholic tastes enable it to feed successfully over a wide terrain and to survive for a considerable time in littoral or desert surroundings. Primarily adapted to feed in shallow water, it overcomes the limitations of such regions in a variety of ways.

It forages throughout the day, being especially active very early and very late; limited feeding is done at night. Observation reveals that the heron has a preference for eels above all other fish; the majority of trout taken are small, and on balance it is probably beneficial to fisheries.

APPENDIX TO CHAPTER 5

Analysis of 32 Pellets from Dam Wood.

1.	59 x 36 mm.	9.70 gm.	Water-vole *Arvicola amphibius* fur and elytra of the beetle *Dytiscus marginalis*.
2.	52 x 24 mm.	8.25 gm.	Water-vole fur and teeth with fragments of a beetle.
3.	54 x 41 mm.	10.50 gm.	Fur, teeth and claws of water-vole, *Dytiscus marginalis* and a length of mare's-tail *Equisetum*.
4.	52 x 34 mm.	9.18 gm.	Water-vole fur and claws, beetle fragments, and an oat.
5.	58 x 39 mm.	9.10 g.m	Water-vole fur and one small beetle.
6.	67 x 37 mm.	11.95 gm.	Water-vole fur, *Dytiscus marginalis* and parts of three other small beetles.
7.	60 x 28 mm.	7.73 gm.	Fur and teeth of water-vole.
8.	51 x 43 mm.	12.95 gm.	Entirely composed of water-vole fur.

9.	58 x 31 mm.	9.44 gm.	Fur and teeth of water-vole.
10.	90 x 26 mm.	15.75 gm.	Fur and teeth of water-voles, with undigested piece of bone.
11.	80 x 33 mm.	9.57 gm.	Composed entirely of water-vole fur.
12.	74 x 33 mm.	10.00 gm.	Fur, teeth and claws of water-vole, with fragmentary remains of beetle.
13.	86 x 33 mm.	7.66 gm.	Contents as 12.
14.	123 x 42 mm.	8.74 gm.	This remarkable pellet is the only example of a feather pellet obtained at Scarisbrick. It contained the remains of a nestling heron, which, from the condition of the breaking quills must have been about fourteen days old. This is discussed on p. 97. The membrane of the alimentary canal was intact and the bones of a wing remained. A small amount of vole fur was also present in this pellet.
15.	114 x 60 mm.	7.19 gm.	Fur, teeth and claws of water-voles.
16.	49 x 31 mm.	7.70 gm.	Fur, grass and twigs.
17.	80 x 32 mm.	3.71 gm.	Beech twigs, rootlets, water-vole fur and a single feather from a juvenile heron. Unlike grebes, adult herons do not present their young with feathers to eat.
18.	81 x 34 mm.	14.38 gm.	Another remarkable pellet collected after a high wind, during which the birds foraged farther afield than at other times. It contained six prawns *Leander serratus,* turned as pink as if they had been boiled. *Dytiscus* beetle, vole fur, beech twigs and bracken.
19.	113 x 36 mm.	8.35 gm.	Composed entirely of water-vole fur.
20.	85 x 36 mm.	10.82 gm.	Fur, gravel, earth, grass and rootlets.
21.	42 x 28 mm.	3.95 gm.	Sticks and grasses with a little mucous matter but no other animal material.
22.	50 x 38 mm.	2.20 gm.	Beech twigs, leaves of beech and mud.
23.	160 x 28 mm.	4.00 gm.	Composed entirely of water-vole fur.
24.	64 x 24 mm.	3.72 gm.	Vole fur and a few twigs.
25.	20 x 14 mm.	0.71 gm.	A single nodule of fur.
26.	19 x 14 mm.	0.55 gm.	Contents as 25.
27.	19 x 12 mm.	0.25 gm.	A single nodule of short staple fur, probably from a field-vole *Microtus.* This is the smallest and lightest pellet of the series.

28.	49 x 20 mm.	2.34 gm.	Fur, *Dytiscus* beetle and bracken.
29.	37 x 27 mm.	0.87 gm.	Water-scorpion *Nepa cinerea,* head of a small beetle and vegetable matter.
30.	94 x 29 mm.	4.34 gm.	Fur, twigs and mucous matter.
31.	41 x 20 mm.	1.22 gm.	Short staple fur and head of *Dytiscus marginalis*. A pellet composed of many small nodules joined by fur.
32.	29 x 22 mm.	1.87 gm.	Vole fur and grass.

CHAPTER 6

BREEDING BIOLOGY: THE EARLY PHASES

THE HERONRIES

IN WINTER the interests of the heron population are best served by dispersal of the individuals. Early in the year however, beginning about 8 February at Dam Wood, the birds start to gather near the heronries.

The situation and size of the heronry depend to a great extent on the richness of the adjacent feeding ground. The food-consumption of a growing heron is probably double that of an adult; a heronry of 15 pairs with about 50 nestlings would therefore need a convenient food-reservoir capable of supplying 130 adults. Because of this temporarily increased need a plentiful food-supply is of primary importance and the limited choice of suitable places explains the herons' preference for estuaries, where eels congregate in large numbers to adjust themselves to salt water before emigrating, and for the slower rivers where water-voles abound. The largest heronries are found where such prey is plentiful and easily procured; fast-flowing streams, holding mostly carnivorous fish such as trout, which are more difficult to capture, generally support smaller colonies.

In Britain herons are almost entirely tree-nesters, building usually in the tops of the tallest trees where the nests are open to the skies. Practically all the heronries with more than 50 nests are situated south of a line between Gloucester and the Humber; where the most popular nesting trees are oaks. At Dam Wood most of the nests are in beech but there used to be some in larch. In the forests of East Prussia spruce is most commonly used, with some nests in fir and oak. Elsewhere elm, alder, yew, holly, palm and eucalyptus have held nests. Indeed there seems to be no limit as to the species of tree which herons may use.

Where large trees are not available quite small ones suffice. James Fisher drew my attention to a heronry on an island in Loch Laxford in 1939, where the nests were in small trees growing up the side of a steep cliff so that some were partly built on the trees and partly on the cliffs; small heronries similarly situated are still of regular occurrence in the Highlands. Patten referred to cliff nests in Co. Kerry, and I have seen a cliff-nest in Pembroke. This type of site is familiar in Scandinavia; Løvenskiold mentions how in Norway the heronries may be on cliffs or in pine, birch or other trees: a colony near Egersund had some nests in birch and some on the cliff-face. Whenever cliff-nesting occurs, small trees growing from the cliff-face are available as support.

Instances of ground-nesting in various parts of Britain are available in the county avifaunas. Harvie-Brown and Buckley mention several cases in the Hebrides and Orkney. Ground-nesting on tiny islets on Irish loughs is not uncommon and Ryves described a ground nest in Cornwall.

Herons have nested in trees in Britain from the time of the earliest records. In Holland, although tree-nesting is more usual, there are many heronries in the marshes. Over much of the rest of the bird's range marsh-nesting is more general. In this country marsh-nesting may have been more prevalent before drainage changed the character of the land. Stevenson (1866) wrote, " Until the last 40 or 50 years, herons did not build exclusively in lofty trees, seeking the vicinity of mans' dwellings, and gathering together in colonies like rooks, but were scattered in pairs over the Fens and Broads, where the nests were placed, sometimes on a lofty alder in a carr, sometimes on the dwarf sallow and alder bushes in the Marsh, or were hidden, like those of the bittern, among the reeds and sedges."

There have been records of isolated marsh nests from many other parts of Britain during the last century. In 1876 the only chick hatched in a nest built on reeds at Littlesea in Dorset was drowned; in 1886 and later nests were occupied simultaneously in a dense reed-bed and in Scots pines at Aqualate Mere in

Staffordshire; while at the turn of the century unfledged young were found in a nest in a Kentish marsh (W. H. Thomas). More recent cases, such as the example described by N. F. Ticehurst of a pair nesting on a pool on Dungeness Beach in company with black-headed gulls in 1907, and a pair which nested in Wicken Fen in 1939, are so rare as to be noteworthy.

Generally, then, a heronry may be of any one (or sometimes two) of the following types :—

(a) a tree-top site.

(b) a cliff-site, usually in association with trees.

(c) a marsh-site.

Much more rarely it may be:—

(d) on dry level ground.

Aberrations from these typical nesting-places are extremely rare. A pair built on the base of the fountain in Kew Gardens in 1907 and although the nest was washed out by the water being turned on, the herons subsequently rebuilt it (Bidwell). The strangest example of abnormality was at Scarborough, where in 1904 W. J. Clarke found a nest at the foot of a tree in a fir-wood, offering many orthodox sites, which was part of an estate where there had once been a heronry. This nest, made of small fir branches, lined with fine twigs, held three young herons. But although undisturbed the herons did not return.

THE NEST

In the reproductive cycle of the heron the nest has a greater significance than in many other species. It is a near-permanent structure to which birds go each spring; in cases where no existing nest is available a token foundation of a few sticks is made. The nest usually endures for many years, its dimensions increasing until its vast bulk, having become too great a weight or too great a wind-stop, finally crashes. Because of continued building the dimensions and weights of herons' nests are very variable; those built and occupied for the first time may not be much larger than rooks' nests; their diameter does not exceed eighteen inches, their weight no more than a few pounds, and some are so flimsily constructed that it is possible to see the eggs through the foundations. Yet these same nests may grow to as much as four feet in diameter and to half-a-hundredweight. I know of some which were big structures in 1939 and were still occupied in 1949. Marsh nests may exceed a yard in diameter and the Dungeness one was fully 30 inches above the water surface. Nests in cliff-faces, however, are invariably smaller than those in trees.

Herons are conservative in their choice of nesting material; branches and twigs are used in tree-top colonies, while reeds, dock-stems and similar vegetation have been used in the construction of marsh nests. Animal hair, feathers, rootlets and seaweed have sometimes been found in the nest-lining; these materials may have been carried in accidentally with sticks, or taken to the nest for roughage. To discover the use of any more unusual material I had to search back to 1899, when a pair at Stoke, in the county of Nottingham, contrived to make a nest of wire.

Although in China entire heronries may be contained in a single tree, it is not usual in Europe for the nests to be crowded together, four or more nests in a tree being exceptional, while over four-fifths of trees contain a single nest. Old records of large numbers of nests in one tree indicate either inaccuracies of past observers, different forestry conditions, or a changed habit of herons. No parallel can be found in recent history to the heronry at Cressy Hall (referred to in Chapter 4) where Pennant claimed to have seen 80 nests in one oak.

DANCE-GATHERINGS AND NEST-OCCUPATION

In some estuarine sites where the nesting woods also provide winter roosts, herons may be seen all the year round; otherwise they are not about the heronries in winter. They do not make periodical visits before the beginning of the nesting cycle, nor are they driven there by that short spell of apparent sexual activity in late summer which causes song-birds to sing and rooks to display. At Dam Wood, in the years 1948-49-50, no herons were seen before February, but from then onwards they gathered for their nesting, increasing in number until the occupation of the heronry was completed.

Before actually occupying the trees the herons assemble and stand on some piece of ground near by. These gathering grounds are at varying distance from the heronries, dependent upon local topography; once having settled the place, however, they return to it as unfailingly as to the heronry. At Dallam the gathering ground is on the mud in Morecambe Bay; at Scarisbrick it is an arable field, where the standing birds are within sight of the nests.

At first two or three birds foregather, but within a few days the group will have grown. On 19 February, 1950 at Dam Wood no birds were at the nests, but seven were standing motionless in the field with necks drawn in, none apparently interested in its neighbours. For long periods they will stand stock-still, all facing in one direction, each silent and detached; there is nothing suggestive of courtship and very little to suggest a social gathering. Gradually the number standing in the field grows, and I have seen sixteen at once in a season when the colony eventually numbered 19 pairs. The number of birds in the field is always considerably less than the number of occupied nests.

It is on the gathering ground that the herons' somewhat primitive dance may be seen. Often I have watched and it has always been started by a new arrival. The ruffs' mock combat is most frequently elicited in the same way although there the similarity ends. In the dance of the ruffs couples of males face each other in mock battle on the trysting ground, sometimes witnessed by a polyandrous reeve and followed by a mating. The herons' dance may be shared by all the birds on the ground, but is a desultory affair of short duration. The incoming bird usually alights with open wings and runs or skips from the rear down the line already assembled, and they, activated by this stimulus, half unfold their wings and execute a few steps forwards. I have never seen the dance develop into anything more, nor has there been any resultant mating; the activity quickly subsides, and may or may not break out again with the next arrival.

Communal gatherings of herons with dancing have been seen in winter. M. D. Haviland saw one on a December day. The largest gathering I have seen on the Scarisbrick ground was 17 on 12 March, 1950. They mostly stood in their usual attitude, but one or two lay flat along the earth. It was a fine fresh day, and the birds gave repeated demonstrations of that rapid zig-zagging descent which they often make when approaching the tree-tops, but which I had not previously noticed above the gathering ground; there was no other display on this occasion.

Throughout February and well into March new arrivals join the party of birds in the field. By the beginning of March there will be herons on the field and at some of the nests; such is the case until occupation of the colony is complete. It is impossible to say whether each newcomer spends a probationary period in the field, or whether the late arrivals go direct into the tree-tops. Occupation at Dam Wood is usually completed by the end of March, though snow may delay laying for a fortnight; but, whatever the weather may be, there is always an interval between the first arrivals at the heronry and the occupation of the nests. The probable explanation of these gatherings is that the birds await the attainment of the physiological condition necessary for successful reproduction: close sociality may stimulate reproductive development (Fraser Darling).

DISPLAY

When F. J. Feilden shot a heron in Wales on 27 February, 1903, he noticed that its legs and bill were of an unusual colour and before the bird was dead wrote down the following description : " Bill from base crimson, blending into orange-vermilion, indian yellow and aureolin at tip. Eye, scarlet outer circle, straw inside. Legs, upper part vermilion, lower yellow spotted with vermilion " (J. H. Salter, 1904). During the next 38 years this phenomenon appears to have escaped notice. In 1941, however, N. Binsbergen, photographing herons near Amsterdam, noticed that the birds which had only just paired or had not yet paired showed blood-red colour in their eyes and on their bills, while those whose nesting was further advanced had eyes and bills of normal colour. " The bills and eyes of the herons whose nests had been destroyed became red again when they were paired anew."

In March, 1944, a Mrs. Gough had a pair of herons under observation at a heronry near Galway, Eire, and noticed that one bird had a bright red bill and feet while its mate was of normal colouring. Two days later the bill of the second bird had acquired a pinkish tinge. Following this observation B. W. Tucker, in an editorial note in *British Birds*, asked for information and in February, 1949, two further papers on the subject were published. The first was a chronological survey by R. F. Ruttledge and other Irish observers from 19 February to 21 April, tracing the rise and fall of the red colour in the feet and bills of herons in Connemara. Tucker (1949) summarised the information received from various sources, as a result of which it is established that " a tendency to develop a reddish or pinkish colouring of bill and legs in the breeding season is at least not uncommon in the heron."

This colour change is not peculiar to the common heron, for similar tendencies have been observed in birds of closely related genera. In the night heron the feet of breeding birds may change from yellow to red, while breeding buff-backed herons may have iris, bill and legs suffused with red.

Throughout the time spent in tree-tops at Dam Wood, I have never seen a heron with an exceptionally coloured bill feeding young. During the early stages, particularly before the birds claim their nests, a high percentage (30-60) of those on the gathering ground appear to have orange-coloured bills while a small percentage exhibit a decided pinkish suffusion on bills and feet. I have watched them under all kinds of lighting conditions and seen herons with bills of normal colour, others which appear suffused with orange or vermilion and bills which seemed to change colour as I watched. Time and time again, accompanied by friends whose observations were in exact agreement with my own, I have watched an individual with bill and feet of normal colour, which became pallid and then suffused with a gradually deepening orange-pink. The transformation took no longer than a minute and the colour reverted to normal in an equally brief space of time. George Edwards made a colour-film of the little bittern in Holland which shows a similar change occurring during a greeting ceremony. A note on the possible physiological basis of such changes is given in *Appendix 2*, the biological significance is that they contribute to the birds' display.

Whenever a bird has feathers developed as a crest, 'ear-tufts,' a ruff, plumes or a train, the function of these ornaments can be seen when their owner is displaying before a mate or a rival. Since, as various authors from Darwin (1871) to Lorenz (1937) have shown, such striking feather features are secondary sexual characteristics evolved to accentuate the bird's display behaviour, the relationship between the types of avian ornament and the display pattern can be understood. In the family of herons there is a diversity of display ornaments and of display patterns, each species having the most prominent plumes where they are best shown in the postures they strike. Thus as Huxley (1923) noted, the egret's display makes much use of the dorsal train, while in the Louisiana heron there is a marked correlation between the postures and neck feathers. The display of the common heron is adapted to make a brave show with crest, neck and pectoral plumes.

When a male heron comes into breeding condition he takes possession of a nest or a site where one will later be built. From this vantage point he renders himself conspicuous as a potential mate by a display involving voice and gesture, and usually manages to attract a mate within a week or two. The solitary male passes many hours at the nest, sometimes rearranging nesting material, or lying across the nest-cup as if covering eggs, but most of the time is spent standing on the nest-rim or a near-by branch. Standing stock-still high in the tree-tops the heron is conspicuous, but when he becomes both animated and vocal the effect is one which no passing female can ignore.

This display, which has been studied and described in great detail by J. Verwey (1930), is really a ceremony of invitation conforming to a regular pattern. Firmly grasping the nest or branch with his claws, the bird stretches his head and neck vertically upwards to their fullest extent, then lowers his neck over his back with the bill still pointed skywards, and finally, by flexion of the legs, lowers his body into the nest. Throughout several days a heron may be seen thus soliciting, the posturing renewed at the approach of every female. When he has extended himself to the utmost he calls *hoo* and continues to gurgle *-oooo* as his head is brought downwards and backwards: if a female comes close he continues his posturing but stops calling. A variant from the pattern described is usual when a female is quite near; then the head is lowered in front of the bird and the mandibles snapped audibly together. Should the female stay he may snap and thrust his bill towards her, but if she flies off he begins to display again with unabated vigour.

A Dam Wood bird had laid the foundations of a nest and there taken up his stance with all the usual posturing, until in due course another bird arrived and stood near him. Then I thought I should see the culmination of the procedure, but after the male had speared towards it several times the newcomer flew to another tree where two pairs were already established. Later the same day she, or another bird, came with obvious intent to stay, whereupon the male made a determined attack and drove her off. As she returned again and again his attacks gradually grew less determined and before the end of the day they were nibbling each other's mandibles so, presumably, he had accepted her.

In species where the sexes look alike the male's first reaction to an approaching female is often the same as his attitude to an intruding male—Verwey suggests that a show of animosity at the outset is the normal result of the heron's being a solitary bird during the greater part of the year: he may not have as yet adjusted himself to the idea of companionship and the urge to have a mate is in conflict with the urge to protect his territory. On my next visit the female was installed at the nest and the male was bringing offerings of sticks. The advertisement had served its purpose.

Thus the female selects the male, for his position within the heronry is fixed and hers is not. That the female does deliberate for a considerable time when two or three males are available, has been recorded by Verwey, who described in minute detail how a female visited each of three available males about twenty times before making her final choice.

With the acceptance of a mate an entirely new phase begins and the ritual changes. The male becomes the stick-gatherer while the female assumes responsibility for adding the new sticks to the nest. The presentation of each stick occasions display. He flies straight to the nest and alights on the rim uttering a greeting-call *arre-arre-ar-ar*; his crest is erect and neck-feathers are raised, giving a thickened appearance to the upper part, while the pectoral plumes are arranged like a large rosette. The female stands on the nest, stretches to her fullest extent, sinks down again and stretches once more; with crest raised she takes the stick and weaves it into the fabric of the nest. These ceremonies always occasion great excitement and sometimes lead to coition. The birds' ritual, however, can easily be upset. A Dam Wood bird carried a stick to the nest and passed it, with the usual ceremony, to its mate; she felt it all along with her bill, but the end of the stick broke off and with a cry she threw the rest of it over the edge of the nest, flew off and did not return for several hours.

Coition takes place on the nest or on a branch, sometimes following the presentation of a stick, sometimes without any introductory behaviour. When there has been a stick it is first disposed of and then the pair generally bite each others' bills. The cock nibbles the feathers on the back of the hen's neck, which she extends horizontally; he then grasps her neck feathers and steps on to her back, maintaining his balance by waving his wings. The female, too, often spreads or waves her wings and when the male flies off she may rearrange a stick in the nest or preen.

Twice during his intensive study of these matters Verwey heard a heron clapper its mandibles. This form of display-behaviour is unusual but I have heard it on rare occasions associated with coition. Compared with the clappering strophes of the white stork the heron's instrumental display is insignificant and probably for that reason has been largely overlooked.

From the time the cock claims a nest there is a certain amount of disturbance from other herons. Little real fighting takes place but the call with which the male accompanies his advertising display may also have a territorial significance. In the event of another heron settling too close to a nest the owner makes an aggressive display. If the occupant is standing on the nest at the time of the intrusion it reaches forward over the nest-rim, brings its head forward to a point lower than its feet, and at the same time snaps its bill. If lying across the nest-cup the same snapping thrust is made but it does not rise; a harsh note and raised crest accompany the thrust. While this performance is usually sufficient to ward off an intrusion, the thrust is only symbolical: the whole performance is a threat-display. The similarity between this posture and a variation of the advertisement display is marked and the crest is raised in exactly the same manner in both cases.

Nesting activity of a symbolical kind unquestionably has a stimulating effect on grey herons. Threat-display may well have the two separate functions of safeguarding the nest, and of helping to stimulate the erotic state of its owners.

Although much bill-thrusting and threat-display are to be seen during the earlier phases in the heronry, running combats, so often evident between neighbours in a rookery, are apparently unknown. As herons sometimes steal sticks from other nests it is surprising that more fighting is not observed.

Nest-relief always occasions great excitement and mutual display: the ceremony follows a definite pattern but there are variations. The general sequence is as follows:— The incubating bird, looking towards its mate, calls *arre-arre-arre-ack*, and stands up; it then lowers itself half-way to the nest-cup and stands again facing its incoming mate with neck up-stretched, crest raised, and pectoral plumes out-spread. The returning bird, having arrived almost simultaneously with wide-spread wings, grasps a branch, calls *arre-arre-ack*, waves its wings and steps on to the nest-rim. There it assumes a posture similar to that of its mate and they stand with bills pointing towards each other, uttering a series of hoarse cries which no alphabet can reproduce. Then the change-over is effected with the relieved bird stepping on to the nest-rim or taking a few running steps across the nest.

Anyone who has watched herons at close quarters must have realised that there are variations from the regular patterns of display. Advertisement, stick-presentation, threat-display and nest-relief all occasion a series of appropriate postures although none is peculiar to any ceremony. For example sticks may be brought at any time from the beginning of the breeding cycle until the young finally leave the nest; there is no clear-cut difference between the presentation ceremony before the first egg is laid and the nest-relief ceremony when small young need brooding. Some of the display postures are extremely grotesque, especially one in which the pair face each other with swollen, rigid necks vertically upstretched and the big rosette-like ornament of the raised pectoral plumes framed by gently-waving wings.

Ceremonial gaping is a familiar form of display in a gullery or a colony of shags but somewhat unexpected in a heronry and has, apparently, been overlooked. This exhibition of the deep flesh-colour of the gape may constitute a threat display, a sexual stimulus or, in the case of young birds, a stimulus to their parents to feed them; and I have watched herons gaping on occasions which did not appear to fit into any of these categories. A pair will gape in a mutual ceremony but I have also seen them gape when alone at the nest; while nestlings will enact exactly the same motions. One day a young bird alighted in the tree above my hide, called *arre* as it stood quite still, then, after gaping two or three times, flew to rejoin three other young birds in the next tree. Whatever their stage of development herons gape in the same way. There are only two movements and the performer may execute either or both. In one movement the bird stands erect with neck outstretched and bill pointing skyward, opens its mandibles to their fullest extent, distends its gullet slightly and exhibits the inside of its mouth and tongue. In the other movement the bird bows its head below the level of its toes and gapes in that position. No sound is uttered.

The Clutch

In favourable weather a few birds lay at the end of February, but the heaviest laying time is in March, and some nests do not contain eggs until May. By calculating back from the time egg-shells are thrown out the principal laying period at Dam Wood can be ascertained as about the third week of March. Observations by J. H. Owen in Essex and at a heronry in Perthshire show there is little difference in the main laying dates throughout Britain.

Usually the birds last to lay are young ones nesting for the first time or old birds which have had a previous clutch destroyed: they may lay in a nest adjacent to one holding well-grown young.

Haverschmidt found that, in Holland, few of the storks which delay their arrival at the nests until May rear young; I find no evidence that the later heron broods actually fail in Britain, although they are generally smaller than average.

When a female stork arrives at the nest before the male she frequently lays a clutch of infertile eggs, replacing them later by a fertile clutch; that I have never known of a parallel occurrence in a heron's nest provides further evidence that it is the cock which arrives first. A heron will sit on an empty nest, before her first egg is laid, but she will not lay before the third and possibly not before the sixth day following fertilisation. The second egg is not laid until two to four days later.

The eggs, slightly elongated, with similar curvature at both ends, are greenish-blue from the bile pigment oocyanin, which is so evenly distributed through the shell that the shade is the same from exterior surface to lining membrane. They are without gloss or further pigmentation: markings sometimes present are due to blood-spots (from parasitic infestation), vegetable staining and, in stored shells, to fungus. All that I have measured, except one, were within the limits given by Jourdain :

Average of 100 British-taken eggs....59.94 x 43.24mm.
Maxima ....66.7 x 45, and 61.5 x 49.7mm.
Minima....53.5 x 43.2, and 59.6 x 40mm.

The exception was a pygmy egg from Dam Wood in 1948. It had been ejected from a nest and still contained traces of yolk; the measurements were 38 x 19mm. Niethammer gives the average weight of 100 German-taken eggs as 60gm.

Clutch-size in Europe varies from one to ten: Knabe examined 203 German nests between Mid-May and 3 June and found an average clutch-size of 3.9. In France the commonest clutch-size is 4, and in Denmark 5, which is in accordance with the observation that clutch-size tends to increase in the northern part of a bird's range. At Dam Wood the median size of clutch in 1937 and again in 1948 was exactly 4, with a maximum of 5 and a minimum of 2. In 1949 the figure was 4+ over a greater number of nests.

Extremes of clutch-size are exceptional. A very small clutch may prove to be incomplete. An extraordinary clutch of 10 was found in a heronry existing until recently at Masserine Park, Co. Antrim. In 1931 the nest held a normal clutch of 5, on 19 March 1932 there were 10 eggs and in 1933 there were 9. In 1934 there was again a clutch of 4 and in 1935 hooded crows robbed the nest while laying was in progress. Whether these outsize clutches were indeed the output of one hen or whether two hens had each contributed a quota one may only conjecture; it is, however, difficult to understand how two hens of this species could lay in the same nest.

Incubation is shared by both birds and they change over during daylight every four to six hours. This labour has been divided on such equitable terms in all cases under my notice that I could usually anticipate the relief time to within a quarter-of-an-hour. The hen alone sits throughout the night. An instance mentioned by Ryves of one adult feeding its mate on the nest is an aberration, to explain the significance of which would involve an examination of the evolution of bill-sparring, which may be symbolic of a former habit of feeding. Incubating herons now obtain their food during off-duty spells and, after incubation is properly under way, the periods when the birds are at the nest together are very short.

The incubation period has been variously recorded as from 25 to 28 days. The length of time between laying and hatching may not coincide with the time between the start of incubation and hatching, for, although incubation most frequently starts as soon as the first egg is laid, it is sometimes delayed until a second or even a third egg has been added, which readily accounts for the discrepancy of a few days. The period between the start proper of incubation and hatching varies only within very narrow limits. In 1947 I verified that the last egg of a clutch hatched 25 days after having been laid, a fact which I have repeatedly confirmed. The incubation period therefore extends only to the 26th day.

If a pair of herons lose their clutch they will lay a second and hatch successfully but it is rare indeed for a pair to rear two broods in a season. Some apparently authentic instances of double broods differ so much that a brief account seems to be called for. I have never known of a second brood at Dam Wood although there have been many broods resulting from second layings.

In 1896 a pair built 60 yards from some cottages in Cork and reared a brood which were fledged by the end of April. On 7 May they began a second nest 30 yards away and the following day one of the old birds was seen driving off the young which were importuning for food. A second brood was reared in the new nest. A similar instance is cited by Verwey; a pair built a second nest while still feeding young and, although they continued to feed them, their attitude was distinctly hostile. Jourdain found an isolated pair in the Waveney Valley, Norfolk, in 926 which, after rearing their chicks, relined the nest and reared another brood. The young were just beginning to fly from a nest, watched by Southern, when he noticed a single egg in it and a fortnight later there was a clutch of six. These cases are exceptional and conform to no pattern; two separate nests may be used, the old one may be relined, or used again without any preparation.

First-year and Unmated Herons

While it is generally understood that the heron breeds for the first time in its second or third year, on 28 May 1935 at Jaschkowen, East Prussia, a female heron which had been ringed as a nestling at the same place the previous May was shot at the nest while feeding young. This confirmed Verwey's statement that he often had seen one-year-old females breeding in the Netherlands and proves conclusively that female herons may be reproductively mature in their first year even though they do not attain adult plumage until they are two years old. Verwey further found that the one-year-old hens do not become sexually mature until at least a month later than fully-adult hens. Niethammer states that the urge of the one-year-old female to build is stronger than the urge to be fertilised; this is undoubtedly true since every heron in the colony, whether adult, one-year-old or brancher shows an urge to build (p. 93). The male does not appear to be reproductively mature until the summer of its second calendar year or even until towards the end of its second year of life, that is in the spring of the third calendar year (Holstein).

Small satellites, odd nests or groups of nests, are often built around a rookery after the main re-occupation. These outlying nests are probably established by young birds breeding for the first time. Similarly in a heronry a second wave of breeding activity is sometimes noted, which, in my opinion, is caused by younger hens coming into reproductive condition. At Dam Wood in 1948 a fresh nest was started fully six weeks after the others, built presumably by a male which hitherto had failed to find a mate and a young female just attaining reproductive condition.

Wherever conditions are suitable adult herons may be found during the breeding season remote from heronries and apparently without sexual desire: the south Lancashire flashes support a regular population of such birds—I have seen many about the waters of Dumfriesshire, Wigtownshire and Galloway, while in the Hebrides and Ireland the non-breeding stock seems to be especially large. These birds, living in isolation, have no effect upon the breeding population, but there are many others which, while remaining mateless, have strong sexual desires and their presence can have a most disturbing influence in the heronries they frequent. The census of heronries in 1928 revealed that the proportion of such non-breeders in the colonies varied from nil to a third.

To judge from their behaviour most of these birds are males, for they not only press their attentions upon the mated females but also disturb their nests and, according to Holstein, sometimes attack nestlings until they die. Although the species is monogamous the males have promiscuous tendencies and the presence of unmated males greatly increases promiscuity. When many are about a colony they must in these ways quite appreciably affect its success but they do not, under any known circumstances, ever become a menace comparable with unmated or nest-seeking storks. These marauders, states Haverschmidt, engage the owners of a nest in battle which may be long and bloody and may cause the destruction of eggs or young.

CONCLUSION

This study of the early phases of the heron's breeding cycle shows how the synchronisation of breeding condition is achieved.

G

The birds, which have been dispersed, return to the vicinity of the heronry and gather on a piece of ground, the limits of which are determined by local topography and the bird's habits. Posture and dance stimulate reproductive condition and when this is attained the males establish themselves in the nests. There by cries and postures they attract the females, which then select their mates. Various formalised displays mutually stimulate the pair and symbolic threat-displays ensure freedom from interference. A principal factor producing a prolonged nesting period is that the female nesting for the first time does not come into breeding condition until later than birds which have bred before. Unmated males in a colony may molest mated females and interfere with young. An incubation period of 25 days, shared by both birds, produces a brood, the development of which is described in the next chapter.

CHAPTER 7

BREEDING BIOLOGY: THE YOUNG HERONS

A RELATIVELY small egg and comparatively short incubation may indicate that the chick will emerge helpless and naked and that there will be a lengthy fledgling period. These conditions all obtain in the case of the heron, and the young birds, after remaining in the nest for eight weeks, spend a further spell about the heronry before becoming completely independent. The following chronological account is based on a study of the brood at one particular nest, made in 1948. I have also described any interesting incidents which occurred at any of five other nests near enough for observation.

Embryonic birds of whatever Order are very much alike. Often, even to the point of hatching, there is little suggestive of the adult form, but the Ardeine character of the heron embryo is apparent several days before hatching. An embryo I took from a broken egg measured 4.5 inches from bill-tip to claw, very large eye-parts protruded from the orbital cavities,

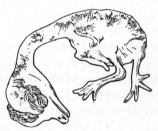

FIG. 5
Embryo heron

and the gape measured 0.8 inch from the hinge to the egg-tooth. A pouch of extremely elastic tissue joined the distal part of the lower mandible to the neck. The thin flexible neck, with no indication of the kink, was disproportionately long, the legs disproportionately short and the body only half as large again as the head. The skeleton was completely cartilaginous.

1st Day. The newly-hatched chick and remaining eggs are so closely brooded that the parent leaves them only for the relief ceremony or if seriously alarmed. It is a curious-looking chick which feebly stretches up its head during the short intervals when the nest is uncovered and in this early stage it lies along the full length of its tarsi. Tow-coloured down is already clear on the down-tracts and its head bears many long filaments which the chick raises like a crest; its upper mandible and the bare skin around its eyes are lavender-grey; its iris is pale yellow, lower mandible yellow and throat orange-yellow.

3rd Day. A second egg-shell below the nest indicates the hatching of another chick. As yet there is little noticeable difference in the appearance of the elder chick and the nest is still closely brooded. After the greeting ceremony, which may include a stick presentation, the newly arrived bird feeds the young as its mate leaves the nest. After feeding it straddles the nest and settles down to brood.

6th Day. Of the three chicks now hatched, the first is decidedly the largest and strongest. They are still brooded continuously except for short intervals during nest-relief, when they are fed. The majority of the nests contain young and there are spasmodic outbursts of sound from dawn till dusk. One or more of the broods may suddenly give utterance, but the din does not extend throughout the heronry and it reaches its crescendo at any particular nest just before and during the visit of a parent. These hunger cries, which are only emitted immediately before, during and sometimes, if there has been no feeding, immediately after a parental visit, might be described as a long series of monosyllables, repeated without alteration of pitch or speed and without break. These cries, which might be written as *yek-yek-yek-yek-yek,* are entirely vocal and produced with the mandibles parted, yet of such a quality as to suggest bill-clappering. They are uttered by young herons from hatching until they fly and never afterwards.

10th Day. All five young have now hatched and the old birds still brood attentively. The nest-relief period, however, lasts longer and feeding-times provide ample opportunity to record the changed appearance of the eldest chick. It is still in down, but quill development beneath the skin is shown by local darkening of the surface; the orange-yellow area on the throat is down-covered and the lavender-grey colour is receding from the distal end of the upper mandible. As the parent prepares to regurgitate it stands over the nest-cup stretching its neck upright and the distension of its gullet is plainly visible.

Herons feed their young entirely by regurgitation. For the first ten days there are long intervals between feeds and much brooding: for the next three weeks feeds are more frequent; thereafter meals are gradually reduced to two or three a day. All food during the first ten days is placed directly into the chicks' gullets although some is spilt into the nest because the chicks grasp the parental bill by the side and not by the tip. Spilt food is picked up by the old bird and either given to a chick or re-swallowed.

14th Day. The quills of the eldest chick show plainly and it preens its down when no old bird is brooding. The five young in the brood are stepped in size like the children of a human family. All raise their crest-down when uttering their hunger-cries and, although not yet inclined to move from the nest-cup, the older chicks have short bursts of activity, chiefly manifest in violent scratching about the nostrils with their middle claws.

During incubation trees and nests remain tolerably clean but, after hatching, conditions rapidly deteriorate so that the stage of development of the broods can be deduced from the state of the nests and their surroundings. Adults generally avoid fouling the nests but the young are less particular: throughout their first weeks they void towards the rim, keeping the actual cup fairly clean, but after they have started to move about they often defecate just where they stand so that the mutings percolate through the nest. The adults cannot clean their nests, for the effluent, a viscid liquid, has no containing capsule.

On hot sunny days the nestlings appear to suffer from the lack of shade and at several of the nests they may be seen sitting with open mandibles and pouches vibrating with rapid panting. Sometimes an old bird stands by the nest with drooping wings shading them. In hot weather I have seen fledged young herons in this same shag-like attitude away from the nest and in late summer old herons will stand thus on the ground exposing a greatly increased surface area to the sun.

17th Day. By this time all the nestlings have made considerable growth and the quills of the oldest are breaking, but the most noticeable change is in their behaviour. They solicit food with greater insistence and to greater effect.

The five young herons at my nest heralded with hunger-cries the approach of their parent. This landed on the nest-rim with a great beating of wings, walked to the centre of the nest and stretched its neck upwards to its full extent. The two largest nestlings, still clamouring, reached up for its bill, which was shortly lowered to them, and eagerly grasped by one young heron at either side. The ensuing rhythmic movements stimulated the old bird to disgorge, and the bill-grasping became henceforward the invariable practice.

An interesting feature of the process of regurgitation is the complete emptying of the stomach: birds which have been shot immediately after feeding young have been examined and found to contain no vestige of food. As might be expected, the process takes a considerable time and is not always completed in a single operation; after its contortions the old bird may rest awhile until more bill-grasping produces a second effort; the hunger-cries and actions of the young while expressing their impatience to be fed also stimulate the process.

A heron is able to retain food in its stomach for lengthy periods, certainly until its discharge is dictated by the brood's requirements. Moreover food is regurgitated in very different stages of digestion according to the age of the young. During the first ten days, when placed directly into the gullets of the nestlings, food is in an advanced state of digestion; as meals at this stage are far apart it has probably been retained a long time to achieve that end. When food is first thrown up into the nest before being given to the young it is friable and disintegrates on impact. Later, food is ejected in a fresh condition, roach, eels and other items being intact and recognisable.

Besides being more active in appealing to their parents in the third week the young herons are no longer in need of brooding. One day in early June during heavy rain at Dam Wood, a nest of young were brooded; the eldest chick aged sixteen days was impatient of being covered and made several escapes from beneath its parent. From that day, they were not brooded again during the daytime no matter how inclement the weather. During frequent heavy thunder-showers, which occurred in 1948 after the brooding period was finished, young herons in all the six nests I could see from the hide stood upright, close together, and suffered no ill-effects. Young purple herons have been known to form a circle during a rainstorm, so that by facing the centre and with their shoulders touching each could shelter its head beneath the tent-like interior (Beetham), but there is no such arrangement in the case of the common heron.

18th Day. Bill-grasping, now the normal stimulus by which a parent is induced to regurgitate, is practised by the young birds amongst themselves. A parent heron returned from fishing and, stimulated by hunger-cries and bill-grasping, brought up an eel which a young bird immediately pulled from its gullet. The eel fell into the nest-cup and was eagerly seized upon by the two larger young herons, one at either end. They swallowed the eel until their bill-tips met, whereupon the stronger bird hauled and swallowed the other half from inside its nestmate, and promptly settled down to sleep, while the other, still hungry, moved restlessly about the nest. Suddenly the hungry bird grasped the bill of its sleeping nest-mate and wrestled until the rhythmic motion induced it to throw up the fish and the other quickly ate it without further interference or competition ! This remains the only case within my experience of a young heron obtaining food from a nest-mate by bill-grasping, but it is significant of the functional relevance of these actions of the young birds to the adults.

20th Day. The plumage pattern of the oldest nestling is beginning to emerge, its neck-markings being quite clearly defined and its primary quills having almost an inch of web; its upper mandible is slate-coloured, the lower one yellow with the pouch off-white. The disparity in the sizes of the young birds is even more obvious: in behaviour too the difference is very marked, for while the younger chicks make no attempt to move from the nest-cup, the older ones are decidedly interested in the edge of the nest. Meals are now occasions of intense activity.

The long intervals between are spent in sleeping and preening; the young birds trim their growing feathers, carefully following each feather-tract, nibbling the quills and generally giving much attention to their plumage.

23rd Day. Having explored the farthermost parts of the nest, the two older young spend much time sitting there preening and stretching, although they anticipate the arrival of a parent by returning to the nest-cup, where all join in a sustained hunger-chorus. Wing-stretching has become a regular exercise: the nestling holds on to the nest with the toes of one foot and extends the other at the same time as the wing on the opposite side. When it has stretched those limbs to its satisfaction it changes its grip and extends the opposite two.

Intervals between feeding may vary from two to four hours, but a chorus of hunger-cries is constantly breaking out at one or other of the nests. It is remarkable how quickly the young recognise the approach of their own parents. As soon as a heron appears in the sky it is identified by its own brood, which will clamour excitedly until it alights on their nest; although neighbouring broods occasionally join in the chorus, only those really concerned keep up the greeting.

27th Day. After the usual bill-grasping to stimulate regurgitation, a fish appeared inside the old heron's gape and a young one inserted its own bill and forcibly pulled it out. Following the meal the old bird retired to a branch to preen; the brood rested for a time and later they too carefully tended their feathers. They now stood to preen, smoothed their backs with their heads, half spread their wings and carefully nibbled the quills. This accomplished, one young bird drooped its wings loosely and vigorously shook its plumage.

From the time they begin to move about the nest the young herons utter another call quite distinct from their hunger-cry. I can only describe it as suggestive of the sounds of a broody hen, except that the heron's voice has an altogether harder tone, rather like that produced by a cord reverberating a piece of taut parchment. It is peculiar to the nestlings and never, I believe, uttered by adults. The young birds combine with it a certain amount of activity, such as shaking out their feathers or bill-grasping, and often their attitude is reminiscent of broody hens, for their wings are depressed and their plumage raised. Sometimes the performance is heightened by a little run across the nest or a few steps round it; when one bird initiates this call the entire brood is likely to take it up and even young in neighbouring nests may join in. The whole outburst, however, seldom lasts for more than a minute.

30th Day. By frequent shaking of their plumage the young herons are ridding themselves of the remaining down filaments, for even the oldest of the brood still has a little down showing between its contour feathers, while attached to each feather of its growing crest is a single filoplume. The primaries and rectrices are still so short that when the young heron stands erect with up-stretched neck it has a bottle-like silhouette. This vertical stance gives herons an advantage over most birds in that it enables them to stand back to wind without having their feathers disarranged: a brood may stand in the nest and face all directions of the compass as if each were set to scan an arc of the horizon.

34th Day. Two branches growing from the fabric of the nest prove very useful to the young herons, which climb out and grasp them while exercising their wings. Day after day these exercises have become more strenuous until sometimes the whole nest shakes. Particularly noticeable, now that the young are becoming more venturesome, is the prehensile use of their bills; as well as grasping with its mandibles, a young heron sometimes lays its bill across a branch either to help in climbing or to prevent a fall. Niethammer states that young herons from nests on the ground leave before they are fully fledged and it is a similarly precocious habit which causes them to scramble about the tree-tops before they can fly.

Whenever a parent returns all the young greet it in the nest, having scrambled back from their precarious " flapping posts." They grasp its bill and pump-handle it until there is no food left inside it; meantime their hunger-cries rise to squeals. Even now an old heron sometimes returns carrying a stick, which it will place on the nest before regurgitating.

38th Day. The nest is in a filthy state with excrement smother-
ing the branches and spattering the bracken below. It seems
strange that as the nestlings grow older they abandon even that
primitive attempt at nest-sanitation which they showed as very
small chicks. There are many dropped sticks on the ground and
the reason is not far to seek. When the adults are carrying sticks
for actual building, very few are lost and even after the nest
appears to be virtually complete the sticks brought as ceremonial
offerings are worked into the structure; but the young, within ten
days of being hatched, begin to pick up and rearrange any loose
nesting material. Presently, in their eagerness to indulge in this
practice, they pull sticks out of the nest and place them in another
position. It is during this activity that so many sticks are dropped
and the number increases vastly after the young are a month old.

41st Day. On this day the first-hatched heron became airborne.
Wing-exercises extend over the entire period the young are in the
nest and after they have left it. Practice begins a few days after
hatching; at a week old they stretch and raise their wings; in a
fortnight they have begun their flapping exercises; in three weeks
they spend much time on the nest-rim and from then onwards
they exercise regularly. From the earlier stretchings there gradually evolves a wing-beat so vigorous that the perch sways in
rhythm, and so rapid as to exceed by far that of a flying heron.
As the pinions grow the bouts of flapping occur at ever-shortening
intervals while more complicated evolutions replace the simple
exercises. Sometimes a bird will leap up and down, or run round
the nest-rim, energetically beating the air with its wings. Another
very precarious-looking antic is performed when a youngster,
having climbed to some distant branch, clings to it firmly while
flapping with such abandon that it seems in imminent danger of
losing its balance and crashing, were it not that, by anticipatory
action, its legs are flexed to counterbalance any movement of its
perch.

45th Day. Two more of the brood of five young herons are
now able to fly from branch to branch of their nesting-tree although they have not ventured over the open space to the next
tree. Several times I have seen a young heron make its maiden

flight. In one instance the bird had been exercising with unwonted energy, when suddenly it took off and pitched on to another branch, where with much scrambling and prehensile use of its bill it gained its balance. After a while it returned to the nest and thereafter with increasing frequency undertook short flights to surrounding branches and later to neighbouring trees.

In another case a brood of two had spent the early part of the day preening, bill-grasping and wing-stretching: then the more advanced one leaped on to a branch where it was accustomed to exercise itself and clung on during a bout of vigorous flapping. In the same tree was a disused nest: the young bird launched itself into the air and landed on the vacant nest. There it collected a stick some 18 inches long which it held between the tips of its mandibles and, burdened with this awkward cargo, embarked on the return journey, stepping delicately across the greenery as far as possible, then bridging the gap to its own nest by half-flying, half-climbing, making prehensile use of wings and feet. The most difficult part of the journey was the final stage, but its nest-mate reached forward, seized its bill and helped to haul it to safety. The two nest-mates then proceeded to work the stick into the nest.

Having the urge to build, it is a natural consequence that the young herons should bring material from outside. I have seen that a young bird's first action away from the nest was to collect a stick and retain it during a perilous journey. From this time the ' branchers,' as the young herons are termed after they get into the branches, bring sticks when returning to their nests and sometimes there is much deliberation as to the best place to deposit the fresh material. Two or three young will hold a twig and try it in various positions before it is finally disposed of or, during an argument, dropped into the bracken. Nest-building by young birds is innate. Thus the habit can no longer be regarded as peculiar to the adults' reproductive cycle.

52nd Day. Now, as during the past few days, there are long periods in which none of our brood of five are in the nest, although two or three may return to preen, or indulge in further nest titivation, and all five still come back to be fed and to roost for the night. The vacant nest in the same tree is very popular and one or two of the young herons spend lengthy periods there. It serves both as a convenient preening perch and as a store of sticks, which a bird frequently pulls out to carry away and build into its own nest.

At Dam Wood I never saw a young heron fly to another nest containing a brood but Knabe experimented in transplanting young herons from one nest to another and found that if one or two chicks ten days hatched were placed in nests containing almost fully-fledged broods, both the original broods and the introduced birds were successfully reared together, which bears out the earlier experience of Bentley Beetham who found that if a young heron strayed into a neighbour's nest it would be fed by its hosts. Beetham saw that not only did the host feed its visitor at the same time as its own brood but also that the parent of the visitor, finding its own nest empty, ignored the other young which were on the branches (for some inexplicable reason not having returned to the nest) and flew to its neighbour's nest, where it fed both its own young and its neighbour's without discrimination. Knabe, too, relates how a heron was seen, after feeding its own brood, to fly farther into the wood and feed another family, presumed to be parentless. It is interesting to contrast Haverschmidt's observations concerning white storks in this connection: when young white storks visit a neighbour's nest they are generally driven off when the owners regurgitate for their own brood.

56th Day. Eight weeks after hatching the young heron is fully fledged, with down remaining only in its crest. It is now an accomplished flier but still comes to the nest to be fed and to roost. For some two weeks after they are able to fly freely the young birds remain within the wood but select perches well away from the nesting trees. A pine with a flat top is one favourite resting place which seems to be regarded as communal, for young from various nests use it simultaneously; the upper branches of a dead oak were regarded as the special property of a trio which moved about together.

About this time the young herons acquire a new note, a low and very short growl, *arr,* uttered once or more with a considerable interval between. Not until the young heron is entirely independent does it develop its adult voice; when I have put up young outside the wood in August they have called exactly like old birds, but while they remain in Dam Wood they make none but the juvenile calls. A young heron strong on the wing will fly to the vicinity of the nest anticipating a meal, perch near others of its brood which have also returned and there converse in low growls—*arr-arr-arr ;* then an adult will fly in and all the brood foregather at the old nest and utter hunger-cries, just as they did when only a few days old, but now to the accompaniment of the music of wildly beating wings. From the strange cacophony in the heronry one can pick out every variety of nestling and juvenile call.

After eight weeks it is no longer possible to keep the birds under the same constant observation and so at this stage the chronological account must end. The exact date at which immature herons become independent is unknown. They are still fed by their parents in the ninth week, but by the twelfth week young ringed birds have been shot far from their place of origin. I have watched in vain for any confirmation of the suggestion that, having vacated the heronry, the old birds continue to feed their young by regurgitating into the water. During the first week in July young and adult herons from Dallam Tower frequent the sandbanks together, while in August I have seen family parties still feeding together on the pools between Dam Wood and the coast.

Various considerations affect the percentage of fledgling herons to fly from a nest as compared with the size of the clutch. Infertile eggs are few and the viability of the embryo great. Over a period of years at Dam Wood I have found that, usually, initial brood-size approximates very closely to clutch-size and, omitting the occasional heavy loss resulting from human interference, hatchability is circa 90 per cent. From 1931-36 in East Prussia Knabe examined 1,200 nests with young and found the average brood-size was 3.78 which, compared with an average clutch-size of 203 nests of 3.9 suggests that only 3 per cent of the eggs failed to hatch. Amongst nestlings, however, there may be a high mortality, and the wastage may continue throughout the fledgling period. In

Holland, according to Verwey, the average number to reach full size is not more than three out of an average clutch of five. R. H. Brown remarked on a similarly high mortality in Lakeland heronries, yet I have known many seasons at Dam Wood when there was so little juvenile loss that from more than half the nests every bird flew.

There are certain stages at which the greatest loss occurs. The first period of vulnerability is during the earliest days and those that survive seem well set until about their third week, when the mortality rate may again rise steeply. Bad weather is one of the principal factors affecting nestling mortality and Frase has shown that after the prolonged period of rain in 1953 and after a keen late frost in May 1935, no more than one or two young herons flew from nests in West Prussia which had held clutches of four or five eggs, while Paton and Pike have recorded that all the nestlings in an Ayrshire heronry were killed during the rains of an exceptionally wet spring.

When incubation starts after the first egg is laid the last chick to hatch is very much smaller than its eldest nest-mate; Holstein and other observers contend that these weaker nestlings frequently fall victims to bullying. The puny newly-hatched chicks may be trampled beneath the stronger young in the scramble for food, although the old birds place their feet most cautiously. Haver-schmidt, having noticed that the youngest member of a family of white storks often disappears, supposes that, having become too weak to beg for food, it is not recognised by its parents and is thrown out of the nest as rubbish. Schüz regards these weaklings as a food reserve, to be reared in a time of plenty, to be eaten in lean times, and he has photographed an old white stork swallowing its youngest chick.

I have seen nothing approaching serious squabbling at Dam Wood until the brood were three or four weeks old, when competition over a meal does sometimes become violent. If the food-supply ran short the weakest chicks might be done out of their share and be the first to die of starvation; the starving would certainly be speeded because in its weakness the chick would no longer be able to stretch up to stimulate the adult to feed it. Yet if food is ample every chick gets its portion and I have seen many broods, though markedly graded in size, attain full growth in complete amity. Such small dead young as I have examined, although bearing no sign of violence, might have succumbed to hunger and exhaustion, but never have I seen older nestlings deliberately maltreat younger ones so as to leave mark or injury.

Cases of cannibalism undoubtedly sometimes occur, for I found a heron pellet containing the remains of a young one. Knabe records a young heron of 2½ pounds which contained parts of another one very little smaller, while yet another fledgling was suffocated in trying to swallow a nest-mate of equal size of which it had gorged the head and neck. These cases did not concern very young chicks; they may have been swallowed as a result of a too energetic bill-grasping exercise and subsequent accident rather than by set intention of fratricide, or they may have been already dead when eaten, their removal by this means providing both a convenient method of disposal and a meal.

Various other hazards beset the fledgling herons and are responsible for a number of casualties. Crows take a toll of very young ones (see Chapter 8). Some die in the nests when almost fledged from some obscure cause, which may be an infestation of intestinal trematodes, as many nestling storks die from such infestations acquired from frogs—their favourite food, and the worms' primary host. Rough weather in late spring may dislodge birds which have reached the ' brancher ' stage: in some years no branchers are blown from the Dam Wood tree-tops while other seasons produce several such accidents. If in crashing the bird breaks a leg or a wing it will not survive long, but if uninjured it may live in the undergrowth for some time before starving. Once a young heron is grounded and unable to fly back to its nest, it will be abandoned by its parents.

The causes of loss having been discussed, there remains for consideration the ultimate output of young herons, but exact information is lacking. At Dam Wood in 1948 and 1949 the average number of young reared from each nest was certainly well over three but the average might be considerably less in heronries disturbed by crows or affected by other adverse factors, and in seasons of less favourable weather. It is interesting to compare the output of the entire stork population in Holland which, from an average clutch of four eggs (as in the heronry at Dam Wood) reared only an average of 1.7 birds for the five years 1941-45.

A low reproductive coefficient is suggestive of a long life. The majority of small song-birds with a high reproductive coefficient have lived their lives, reproduced and died, before the age when most herons attain breeding condition. Yet there is a great wastage of immature herons, for a large percentage perish before they are of breeding age.

I have collected from German sources (Frase, Knabe, Kuhk, Lohrl, Prescher, Sager) details of 1,140 recoveries of ringed herons: they are considered first-year birds up to April 20 of the year after they were hatched; after that date they are classed as second-year birds and so on with each ensuing 20 April. A summary shows that 78.6 per cent perished in their first year, 13.6 in their second, 3 per cent in their third and only 4.8 per cent survived to their fourth year or longer. It is interesting to compare these German recoveries with a similar analysis of recovered herons ringed in Britain, 20 April again having been taken as the start of each subsequent year.

Total.	1st	2nd	3rd	4th	5th	6th	7th	8th	9th	10th	11th	12th	13th	14th	16th
252	175	27	20	6	7	7	1	4	1	1	1	0	0	1	1
%	70	10.7	8.0, and 12 in all the subsequent years together.												

If we allow that recovered ringed birds represent a fair sample of all herons fledged, certain conclusions may be drawn from these figures. First, of the young herons that fly from the nests, seven out of ten perish within a year of hatching. This figure is much the same in both British and German recoveries. The British table further suggests that only one out of every five young herons to leave the nest attains breeding age, but that thereafter the wastage is small.

Keysler wrote of a heron that lived for 60 years, the most extravagant claim of longevity for the species and certainly untrue; there is a record in the *Annual Register* for 7 July 1767 wherein we read, "As the Prince Stadholder (of Holland) was taking the

Frank A. Lowe

Plate 5. Adult heron arrives to feed the brood and displays to its departing mate

Plate 6a. Brooding in hot weather, a heron lowers its wings to screen its brood. (*Eric Hosking*)

b. Preening. (*Eric Hosking*)

diversion of hawking he caught a heron with a brass inscription round its legs setting forth that he was taken by the Elector of Cologne in the year 1737." Two further old records are worthy of mention; Brodrick and Salvin wrote of a heron taken in 1844 in Norfolk which had been ringed in the same area 15 years earlier, and another ringed in Holland in 1850 was shot in Algeria in 1858. In foreign zoos a heron has occasionally reached an exceptionally old age: Buttikofer recorded that a captive heron lived for 22 years in Rotterdam Zoo; at Giza, in Egypt, one died 2 April 1922 aged 20 years 3 months 27 days; at Trivandrum one was still living at 21.

In Britain three herons have been recovered which merit special notice: No. 19, ringed 28 May 1910 at Cheadle, Staffs, was recovered in the same county on 27 February 1926, 15 years 9 months after having been ringed. This is by far the greatest age recorded for a wild heron in modern times. No. 112262, ringed 25 June 1933 at Kilbarchan in Renfrew, was recovered in Ayrshire in February 1947. No. 114529, ringed 9 May 1935 at Crofton in Cumberland, was recovered in Cambridgeshire 16 August 1944. Only one heron out of 1,100 in Germany reached its ninth year while from Denmark there is a further record of a bird aged 8 years 10 months. The average duration of life of 23 captive herons in the London Zoo was 28 months and two have survived there for 11 years.

After the young become independent, changes both psychological and physiological occur in the old herons and the colony breaks down. We have seen that perhaps one in five of the young birds may live to breed somewhere and that we may expect a high percentage of the breeding stock to breed again. We are left with several questions. Will those young birds return to nest in the heronry of their origin? Will the surviving old herons use the same nests as previously? To what extent will the pairs of the preceding year come together again? Alas, in spite of all the herons that have been ringed in the countries of Europe we cannot answer any one of those queries completely. Seldom is it possible to read the number on the leg of a living bird and, happily, observers are loath to shoot herons at their nests.

H

Ringing, in Britain and in Germany, has shown that some herons return to the colonies in which they were hatched. A nestling ringed at Harbottle in Northumberland on 17 April 1913 was nesting in the same place in April 1918 and other similar records could be given. Furthermore, recoveries suggest that a considerable proportion of continental herons return to their place of origin, although others move to distant heronries. More precise information is lacking and no one can say, as is recorded of the white stork in East Prussia, that 37 out of 60 identified individuals were nesting for the second time in the same nest.

There is even less evidence as to whether the partners of a previous nesting remate. It is known that some small song-birds may have as many different mates in a season as they produce clutches of eggs, but every clutch is laid in a new nest. We have seen the heron's nest as a long-term institution; that being so, it seems reasonable that the male bird, having returned to the gathering ground and the same heronry, might return to the same nest. Where there is such an attachment to a site it must frequently happen that the hen which is attracted to the advertising male is, in fact, its partner of the year before and, having the strongest attachment to the nest, it would be likely to persevere the most against the initial unwelcoming behaviour of the male.

CHAPTER 8

RELATIONS WITH OTHER SPECIES

THE RELATIONS between herons and other creatures are largely determined by competition for food and nesting sites; it is not regularly preyed upon by any other species although occasionally it is the victim of piracy and is the potential host of certain parasites.

Through the centuries herons have often shown a preference for nesting places in proximity to human habitations but there the association has ended. Since man has ceased hunting the heron for food, or for the sport of falconry, he is only hostile when he considers his fishing interests are menaced.

Pennant referred to a belief that a maimed heron was apt to strike at the fowler's eyes, while there appeared in *The Field* of 26 March 1870 a letter from the Vicar of Nether-Witton, in Northumberland, giving an account of a heron which attacked a farmer; it seized him by the nose and had to be strangled before it would desist. Even to this day the belief persists that a heron will strike at the eyes of anyone interfering with it. A wounded heron should be approached with care for, in such plight, it follows the dictum that attack is the best defence. Young herons fallen from the nest back away from human approach until cornered, when they invariably strike with great speed, usually in the direction of the face, when it is well to remember that they have a remarkably long reach and that the eye is an avian target.

The most diligent enquiry reveals no concrete evidence of mammals preying on herons although it has been suggested that a fox may have been responsible for some heron remains found at Scampton, in Yorkshire. Relationship with the otter does not extend beyond an occasional association on a river; they are not truly competitiors, for the heron takes its greatest toll from the shallows while the otter ravages the pools. It is not inconceivable that an occasional heron may fall victim to the otter and I have an example of one with its rump torn away, supposedly by an otter, though in my opinion it is too wary to be regularly preyed upon.

Small mammals are all fair game. Young rabbits, water-voles, field-voles, mice, moles and shrews, even the smaller carnivores, are all likely to provide a meal for a heron. Domestic animals seldom come within the heron's sphere but I have a record of a kitten having been swallowed by a captive bird, while an adult cat was chased by two herons near a mill-dam at Chichester.

The heron's attitude to birds may be that of a bird towards its prey, of a competitor for a nesting or feeding site, or merely the neutral association of neighbours. Skirmishes between herons and other birds are usually the result of one of these competitions, but they seldom end fatally. Eagles and the larger hawks rarely come into close contact with herons in Britain, although in Scotland golden eagles have occasionally been known to attack them. Nevertheless the only evidence of an eagle's having killed a heron was the presence of a heron's leg-bone in a disused eyrie. Peregrines are of course capable of killing herons, as they were used for that purpose in falconry. In the *Supplementary Report on the Heron Census,* mention is made of a case in which a pair of peregrines attacked and killed a heron above a Somerset peat-bog, but many times I have seen herons pass peregrines without interference. The only instance I can find of peregrines affecting a heronry is cited in the census of the now extinct colony at Birch, Essex—" the continual presence of a pair of peregrines was held responsible for the migration of the entire colony to another site." On the continent, where peregrines are more numerous than in this country, they often nest in the heronries and a state of neutrality exists. Knabe records that in 1938 peregrines nested in 8 out of the 18 heronries in the state forests of East Prussia.

Although I have no evidence that harriers take either the eggs or young of marsh-nesting common herons in Europe, marsh harriers have been known to eat the eggs of bittern and the young of glossy ibis. I therefore see no reason why those of the heron should be immune.

Rooks are certainly herons' greatest competitiors for nesting sites and at many heronries there is also a rookery which may be clearly separated or the nests of the two species may be intermingled. In the main they may be found on reasonably good terms although at times competition for a particular part of the jointly occupied wood has become so acute that serious warfare has broken out. The classical example of a series of competitive conflicts is undoubtedly the Dallam Tower heronry where, during the last century and a half, there have been three major conflicts. The first battle, according to John Heysham M.D. of Carlisle, took place in the spring of 1775. One of two groves by the park was occupied by herons and the other contained a large rookery; the two species maintained a neighbourly neutrality over a long period, until the old oaks in which the herons nested were cut down. Many broods were destroyed by this felling and the herons immediately proceeded to build new nests; in the absence of suitable trees elsewhere, "they determined to effect a settlement in the rookery: the rooks made an obstinate resistance; but, after a very violent contest in the course of which many of the rooks and some of their antagonists lost their lives, the herons at last succeeded in their attempt—built their nests—and brought out their young." The next season there was another battle in which the herons held their ground; thereafter the rooks relinquished the part of the grove occupied by the herons and the two species lived in neighbourly harmony until 1866, when the herons had increased to such an extent that they tried to encroach upon the rookery, but on that occasion the rooks got the better of the day. The most recent battle, the late agent told me, took place a little before the First World War. These erstwhile antagonists now show a splendid tolerance for each other.

Elsewhere many cases have been noted of rooks and herons having come to blows over nesting accommodation. Rooks do not make blameless neighbours; I have seen them steal eggs from other rooks' nests and I have known them pull sticks from herons' nests. Conversely herons are quite prepared to use sticks collected by rooks and there have been instances of their incorporating entire rooks' nests into their own. It may well be that we see in mobbing a recrudescence of such periodical jealousies as led to the battles of Dallam.

Crows, both carrion and hooded, take herons' eggs and young. In some north country sites robbery by carrion crows must have a considerable effect upon the heron population. On the north Lancashire mosses, where a few herons continue to breed, a high proportion of the eggs are sucked, which may also happen in the Suffolk fens. Many heronries in continental Europe suffer greatly from the depredations of crows.

Although herons are largely individualistic they will sometimes make concerted attacks upon intruders and go outside the heronry to drive off crows. In spite of this hostility it is not unknown for crows and herons to have nests in adjacent trees; in Ireland hooded crows have been close neighbours with herons although there has been the usual display of animosity whenever the crows moved: while the birds are actually on their nests an uneasy truce is observed. Crows lose no opportunity of filching herons' food; the census describes the strategy employed by a pair of crows in North Wales, to deprive a heron of a trout. Five or six made an unsuccessful attempt to rob a heron of a mole on the washes near Peterborough.

In Devonshire, in Scotland and in Wales, ravens have been known to share a nesting wood with herons, and they appear to be much better neighbours than crows. The raven forages over a wider territory than the crow and is not such an inveterate nest-robber. A favourite food taken to its young is sheep placentas. I have no evidence that ravens take herons' eggs, but they may harry the herons when they are returning to their nests, although once they settle a state of neutrality is restored. That this is not resented is shown by the fact that the herons return the following spring: sometimes the ravens return too. In Devonshire a pair of herons reared a brood in a nest that ravens had vacated. In Pembrokeshire I saw ravens make repeated sallies against herons which passed on their way to a nest in a cliff; these attacks, however, were of short duration, amounting to nothing more than a few passes.

I do not consider the magpie or the jay to have much effect upon the welfare of the heron in spite of their stealing an occasional egg. Strijbos identifies the magpie as a robber of herons' nests in Holland and it has been accused of similar misdemeanours in north Lancashire, while the jay may have been guilty of like depredations. Several times I have seen herons and magpies living in close association and agreeing remarkably well. In one case a pair of magpies nested in the same tree as a pair of herons in Savernake Forest, young being successfully reared in both nests although only ten feet apart. In another instance magpies built in a tree with two pairs of herons. The strangest associations of this kind were two cases of 'flat-nesting' in which the herons provided cover for their neighbours while suffering no ill thereby. I saw one at Dallam Tower many years ago; among the normal herons' nests there was one very deep structure, the upper storey of which was occupied by a pair of herons while the base served as the roof of the magpies' nest. In this combined nursery herons and magpies fed their young, but although I wondered what would happen when both species visited the ménage together I never saw them arrive at the same time. A similar instance was noted by F. J. Brown at Crewe Hall. Magpies and jays have only very recently invaded Dam Wood; so far, apart from an unsuccessful attempt to take possession of the herons' favourite roosting-tree, there has been neither interference nor association.

There is little evidence that the jackdaw has any predatory intent in a heronry except for an old record concerning a small offshoot of the once-flourishing Findhorn heronry. The herons started to leave Altyre in 1850, deserted it entirely in 1863, apparently because of their eggs being stolen by jackdaws which lived in great numbers in the rocks opposite the heronry. According to St. John "the keeper took handfuls of the shells of the herons' eggs out of some of the jackdaws' holes: the injury to the heronry from this cause must be very great, as the plundering seems to be incessantly going on." Jackdaws have not yet invaded Dam Wood but large bands breed in the old timber and limestone surrounding Dallam Tower. However, their behaviour towards the herons is blameless, as would seem to be the case at Combermere and other

places where large numbers of daws breed near a heronry.
J. H. Owen, who has been watching herons for over 40 years,
told me that he once knew of a pair of jackdaws utilising the
basement of a heron's nest; the daws' comings and goings were
unaffected by the presence of the herons at their nest above.

Cases of intimate association between herons and other birds
are not common. Generally those are instances of small birds
living within the heron's nest, benefiting by the shelter afforded
and living innocuously below their neighbours. Owen has seen
house-sparrows, great tits and starlings in residence in occupied
herons' nests, as well as tree-sparrows, which, of all birds, are
most frequently to be found in such association. Between the
wars a considerable proportion of the herons' nests at Dam Wood
provided shelter for tree-sparrows; this was also the case, although to a lesser extent, at Dallam Tower. Adult herons completely ignored the tree-sparrows, even when they sat on twigs
level with the nest; occasionally, however, the nestlings lunged
at them as they would at flies.

Breeding herons pay little attention to any smaller species
which elects to use their basements, or any part of the tree below
them. Starlings may nest in holes a few feet below with impunity
and woodpeckers running up the trees merely evoke a passing
curiosity. For the strangest of all nest associations in a heronry
I am again indebted to J. H. Owen, who tells me that on one
occasion he knew a couple of long-tailed field-mice to breed in
a heron's nest. That herons eat mice does not preclude the association, for it is common for creatures to live in the proximity
of others which in different circumstances would prey upon them.

Territorial competition sometimes occasions a skirmish and
the kestrel seems to be more given to heron-harrying than the
larger hawks. My notice has been drawn to various instances of
this and one in particular of the Bela, near Dallam Tower, is
interesting. There was a kestrel's nest in an old tree overlooking
a shallow much favoured by herons; whenever a heron settled
there the kestrels would leave the nest and, stooping viciously
towards it, drive it some distance away before allowing it to alight
and feed in peace, generally near the salt water. J. W. Seigne

described a similar incident in Ireland, although his heron was less fortunate, for when it had eluded the kestrels a flock of rooks rose from a nearby field and pursued it. I have frequently seen running combats between sparrow-hawks and the Dam Wood herons. E. W. Hendy described how a pair of merlins successfully chased a heron from the neighbourhood of their nesting site on Exmoor.

No consideration has so far been given to the neighbours and depredators of herons in other than orthodox tree-sites. In the remoter parts of the British Isles cliff and rock nests bring the heron into an entirely different biotic environment; in such cases its neighbours may be cormorants, shags, gulls or even fulmars. At the present time there does not appear to be in these islands any considerable mixed nursery of herons and cormorants such as the one which existed in Co. Mayo reported by Ussher and Warren. In a mixed colony at Poyntz Castle, Pembroke, the herons, according to Mathew, were expelled by the cormorants.

In Europe, common herons nest on excellent terms with pigmy cormorants, and mixed colonies of different heron species are widespread and some are very large. Common herons, purple herons, night herons, squacco herons and little egrets all join in varying degree both in tree-top and marsh heronries in which the affairs of the mixed community progress to a satisfactory conclusion. Certainly herons are gregarious in the breeding season not only with their own species but with birds of closely allied species and even other genera.

A beater on a West Riding grouse-moor told me that herons feeding in the becks would get up when the beaters approached and their low flight over the moor so frightened the grouse that they either froze and refused to take wing, or scattered so quickly in all directions that the guns had no chance to get them. I have never heard herons accused of harming grouse, but a Yorkshire keeper tells me that the presence of a peregrine on a moor puts all the game down and any other large-winged bird produces a similar effect. In Dumfriesshire I met a keeper who said herons frightened wild duck off the water; perhaps this belief persists from the days of the decoy when, according to Folkard, "none of the feathered tribe cause the wildfowler so much annoyance as the heron—its senses of hearing, smelling and seeing at long distances are so extremely acute that its ever watchful nature is almost certain to detect the presence or approach of man, especially in still weather; and when the wildfowl at a decoy are quite unconscious of danger, it sometimes raises an alarm, and instantly every bird leaves the pond." Folkard's reference to the heron's superior sense of smell is an error on his part, for even today little is known about the olfactory perceptions of birds.

Encroachments on an established feeding place may cause discord between herons and waterfowl. Very exceptionally herons may kill adult ducks; there is a case quoted in the census, where a farm bailiff at Lancing College states that he saw a heron killing ducks and tearing open their crops for the food they contained (though it is difficult to conceive that any heron would be reduced to feeding on macerated grain). The late Viscount Powerscourt wrote, from Co. Wicklow, that many of the various kinds of waterfowl that he kept there were being killed and it was some time before he could discover the cause. Introduced bar-headed geese were said to have been systematically murdered, shortly after their arrival, by a puncture of the jugular vein, "and they all had the two marks in their throats where the points of the heron's beak had struck them, and they had all bled to death [As the method is as unusual as the prey I believe the heron was a scape-goat for some unseen killer]. As to the destruction of freshly hatched broods of various kinds of ducks, the herons simply dived down on them and swept them off the water as soon as they appeared." Sir Bartle Frere also sent me an eye-witness account of a heron taking mallard ducklings this way.

A letter to *The Field* in 1909 from Lord Lindley's head gardener at East Carleton near Norwich, described an attack by a heron on nesting mute swans, which ended fatally for the cob. In the gardener's opinion the heron had designs on the swan's eggs, but in the course of extensive research I have not been able to discover a single instance of herons taking eggs.

The foregoing incidents are not intended unduly to stress the fact that a heron may occasionally kill waterfowl; for the very reason that they are instances of exceptional behaviour they tend to be over-emphasised while the normal peaceful relationships pass unnoticed. At times many herons will concentrate on a rich feeding ground and forage together peaceably, often surrounded by small waders and displaying no animosity. On the other hand, when food is scarce, a heron may be extremely jealous of its feeding territory. In such circumstances the rivalry between herons is greater than the rivalry between herons and other species.

Sometimes an attack has been made by one heron upon an-another for which no feasible explanation can be made. One such case concerns two birds, one fully adult, the other a bird of the year, which had fed together from a canal bank for some days until one morning the old bird viciously attacked the younger one, driving it from the water with a great show of animosity. The next day, however, they resumed their former amicable association and continued to feed for several more days from the same reach of the canal. Another case concerned a fight to the death between two herons on 17 December 1941 on the Kent estuary in West-morland; they fought desperately in the shallow water, the aggressor standing over its victim, repeatedly striking it and inflicting wounds from which it died. It should be noted that in this, the only instance of a fatal combat I know, the victim was also a bird in its first year.

Environment influences the relations between herons and other species. No gathering could be more amicable than the associ-ation of curlews, small waders and herons searching for marine organisms on the sandbanks in Morecambe Bay, yet on the moors curlews have been known to mob passing herons persistently and I have seen lapwings stoop resolutely at herons foraging over the mosses near Dam Wood.

Herons and gulls are frequently in association but their re-lationship is complex. At Dam Wood any number up to a score of herring-gulls and lesser blackbacks may fly around more or less continuously; occasionally a gull will chase an incoming heron, but for the most part they ignore each other. The meetings are not always so free of incident, for I have a note of a heron striking a black-headed gull to the ground while both were in flight by a heronry near Nottingham and I have often seen black-headed

gulls mob herons. At Cley greater blackbacks have been seen
chasing herons until they regurgitated and I have watched lesser
blackbacks chivvy them with the same result. It would appear
that many greater and lesser blackbacks have learned to exploit
this particular kind of piracy and profit by the food the herons
disgorge. These sporadic attacks, however, should not be regarded
as the habitual attitude of the gulls to herons.

Wm. Hewitt wrote in 1849, concerning the heronry at Coley
Park, Reading, that although fish were formerly to be picked up
on the ground beneath the nests, he had lately not succeeded in
finding any such remains. The changed circumstance was explained by the presence of otter tracks, "which were evidently
made by those animals frequenting this spot in quest of food
obtained at so little cost." To confirm this particular form of para-
sitism I paid special attention to the matter at Dam Wood and
Dallam. Vomits periodically appeared below the nests, where they
lay until disposed of by beetles and blow-flies; and I cannot find
the slightest evidence of any vertebrate having been attracted into
a wood by the presence of carrion.

The presence of a heronry has very little direct effect on the
wild life of the wood at lower levels. A dearth of small birds is only
attributable to the herons in so far as their presence may have
affected the carpet and undergrowth. At Dam Wood there are the
usual inhabitants to be expected in a mixed wood and bracken
association. The pheasants, ertswhile artificially maintained, have
practically disappeared, but blackbirds, wrens, chiffchaffs, redstarts, woodpeckers and doves remain. The only vertebrate whose
presence might be attributable to the herons is the tree-sparrow.

Note has been made of the heron's propensity for taking
ducklings, yet in a Scottish heronry in the Forth area eider-ducks
have bred since 1910 if not earlier. Previously they nested in the
links at Tynninghame but they were so harried by crows that many
ducks chose to breed in the nettle-beds in the heronry and some
actually laid at the foot of trees occupied by herons.

I believe it is quite exceptional for small birds to mob a heron
as if it were a cuckoo or an owl but T. H. Harrisson saw one
mobbed by swallows and house-martins. The only time that I

have seen any such action by small birds was on the Thames, below Abingdon; the heron was wading by a sluice with black-birds, finches and tits chattering around it; the heron completely ignored them and only flew on my close approach: as I failed to find any other cause for the commotion I concluded that they were mobbing the heron.

I have discussed several instances of other birds living within the shelter of the heron's nest but I have been unable to discover any positive case of symbiosis, which implies a mutually beneficial association, although the tree-sparrow might possibly fit into such a relationship by keeping down the flies.

The heron is host to many parasites. The feather or biting lice (Mallophaga) which have been found on the common heron are *Ardeicola ardea* and *Ciconiphilus decimfasciatus*. Not all herons, how-ever, are infested, for I have examined a number which have proved entirely free from external parasites. A sick bird brought to me early in 1953 had a very heavy infestation all over its body of Mallophaga, identified by Theresa Clay as *Ciconiphilus decim-fasciatus*. Among the creatures taken by H. Britten from nestling heron carcases I sent him was a mite parasitic on a carrion-feeding beetle but no true heron parasites were found on these juveniles. Others living externally on the heron are dipterous parasites (*Pupipara*). The blood-sucking common louse-fly *Ornithomyia avicularia* is a frequent nuisance at the nests of many species, including the heron.

Herons in full vigour appear to be well able to withstand the drain of such internal parasites as may infest them. I have taken worms from sick birds and in 1878 Von Linstow named 16 helm-inthic parasites in the heron. Niethammer lists 18 species of Trematodes, 8 Cestodes, 5 Nematodes and 2 species of Acantho-cephalids, 33 species of worms said to have been taken from the heron.

The attitude of one species towards another cannot always be defined in fixed terms, as it may vary with the prevailing circum-stances. It will be seen from the foregoing examples that this is particularly true in the case of the heron and that the nature of its relationships with other creatures may be affected by various conditions. As a gregarious nester it requires a very small breeding territory, for although the majority of pairs nesting in Britain have a tree to themselves, as many as five pairs will breed agreeably in the same tree with birds of other Orders nesting in the closest proximity, even to the extent of using the base of the heron's nest to conceal their own. Amongst those species which enter into these close associations are birds which may mob the heron or steal its eggs and, alternatively, animals which in other cases may be the heron's prey. There is, surprisingly, nothing exceptional in the fact that a creature may enjoy a temporary asylum in the immediate neighbourhood of the breeding place of another creature which normally preys upon it.

Away from the heronry, a focal point of intense emotional behaviour, there is a readjustment of the heron's attitude towards other species. So long as it can satisfy its hunger on the food it normally takes it is little inclined to interfere with any other creature, but if hungry it regards any animal it can swallow as a potential meal. Thus we find a heron resting on a sandbank closely surrounded by a score of small waders, whereas, if starving it would eagerly make a meal of any of them. While in one place herons will deliberately visit a haunt of sea-birds to feed upon their chicks, they will habitually pass another on the way to some more distant feeding ground. Jealousies occasioned by encroachments on feeding territories have been known to cause attacks on adult waterfowl otherwise outside the heron's consideration. Even between heron and heron squabbles may occur at a feeding ground. An abundance or scarcity of food will cause concentrations and dispersals. Opportunities for collective hunting are infrequent and birds may use forcible means to feed alone.

CHAPTER 9

MECHANICS OF FLIGHT AND DISPERSAL

THE FLIGHT of a heron gives a misleading impression of slowness and deliberation, for the bird is capable of a fair turn of speed, can cover long distances, and on occasion executes complicated aerobatics. I have counted the wing-strokes with the aid of a stopwatch and found that, irrespective of the speed the bird was making, the beat was always between 120 and 130 to the minute, or just over two beats a second.

The wing-beat of most birds is too rapid to be timed by such simple means but the Aeronautical Society of Great Britain had tables compiled by J. D. Fullerton, from all available sources, which included the rate for many species obtained by cinematography and other means. Only the white stork, with a rate of 1.75, has a slower wing-beat than the heron: just as much movement is likely to give an exaggerated impression of speed, so is the converse true.

I have gone to some trouble to assess the heron's speed. One day when going to the Scarisbrick heronry at a steady 30 miles per hour I found myself travelling parallel to a bird flying in the same direction and at the same speed. Similar observations made in Lakeland gave a flying speed of 28 miles an hour. Most herons travel within 500 feet of the ground and within that comparatively narrow belt wind variation is not generally great; indeed actual measurements made by aircraft speedometers from machines flying parallel to the birds and at the same height have shown speeds differing very little from those estimated from the ground. It has been ascertained that mallard, wood-pigeons and herons fly at average true airspeeds of 48.5, 35 and 31 miles an hour respectively.

From the ground height is even more difficult to estimate than speed and it is seldom that two observers will agree. Once it was erroneously thought that migrating birds attained astronomic altitudes of the order of 40,000 feet, and flew at speeds up to 240 miles an hour. We owe to aviation the knowledge that a goose may fly at 50 miles an hour at 7,000 feet, but the greatest height I can find at which a heron has been checked against an altimeter is a little below 2,000 feet above ground-level. From long watches in my tree-tops I am convinced that a heron's normal comings and goings at the heronry are mainly confined to a height not exceeding 150 to 200 feet.

Herons approach Dam Wood from the fields in a routine pattern. A bird rises from the ground, arching its neck and drawing back its legs as it gains height, makes a circuit of the wood, then suddenly turns in to approach in a long effortless glide. As it nears its objective its primaries are spread and stalling is achieved with little other apparent motion. The neck is extended, crossed feet are dropped in readiness to grasp a branch and the heron perches close to its nest. The first five primaries are all emarginated (cut away in a slanting direction) in some degree on the inner or outer web, or on both, so that they provide ample slotting in the broad wings.

In taking off or alighting a heron dangles its legs, but only if it does not intend to travel far, as between the nest and a preening perch. For a longer flight the neck is drawn back as soon as the bird launches itself so that the head is close into the shoulders and the bill, usually slightly uptilted, points forward. The legs are pressed back until parallel with the tail; the feet, placed one above the other to form a ' V,' make a streamlined stern, while the hind claws are held erect; the whole attitude is designed to offer the least resistance to the air. The tail is used to keep the bird's balance when banking for a turn and when the keel is other than central, and it is possible that the upturned toes assist the bird's evolutions, for they are held vertically all the time it is in full flight. The bastard wings are at right-angles to the plane of the wings when a bird is preparing to alight.

Between trees and feeding places herons fly straight and level

Plate 7a. Young herons soliciting food: the thickening of the adult bird's throat shows that food is being regurgitated. *(Photographs by Frank A. Lowe)*
b. A young heron doing wing exercises.

Plate 8. Heron over its heronry

with their usual two wing beats a second, although they sometimes return very much higher and descend at a tremendous rate. In America J. S. Huxley saw Louisiana herons *Hydranassa tricolor* 'shoot' down to their heronries from a great height in a most spectacular fashion; and while they have had young in the nests I have seen common herons precipitate themselves nestwards with widespread wings, turning first one way and then the other with a resultant descent as erratic as it was speedy.

A common variation in a heron's flight is the spiral ascent usually used to evade attack; it was indeed the flight which so delighted falconers but it is not occasioned only by the presence of a hawk; in the Welsh hills chivvying curlews have driven a heron so high that it finally disappeared from sight. An attacked heron will always soar to safety rather than enter into combat. Perhaps the most remarkable instance of aerobatics was seen on a sunny May day in Essex. The heron rose from a marsh and making use of a moderate wind spiralled to perhaps 1,000 feet: thereafter, without any further apparent wing-motion, it gained height until almost out of sight and during the ascent it twice looped the loop.

It is doubtful whether the average foraging range of nesting herons reaches ten miles, but individuals travel a great deal further. Several observers have mentioned herons on St. Kilda (W. Eagle Clarke, 1912) and I saw one which regularly came there to fish in Village Bay, presumably from the Outer Hebrides over forty miles distant, but it did not remain on the island (Lowe, 1934). Fraser Darling has recorded herons visiting Priest Island, off Wester Ross, to feed upon the chicks of the herring-gulls; there the nearest heronry is on the Fionn Loch, close on twenty miles away. Yet all these island visitors could have been non-nesting birds. Indeed on some of the wilder parts of the British coastline herons may be found living an almost maritime existence, depending for their meals on the tidal flats and rock-pools. This mode of life, while giving the impression of an individual having an unusually extensive feeding range, may have quite a different explanation (see pp. 57-58).

The herons at Scarisbrick feed within a radius of six miles where they have access to fresh and salt water, including tidal streams, ponds, canals and a stretch of coastline. Observations from the air around a Cumberland colony showed that the birds foraged commonly up to eight miles distant and even up to eleven miles, but for the most part they would remain within four miles of the nesting trees. During these observations R. A. Carr-Lewty noticed that the birds tended to forage into wind, which is the normal procedure. The only occasions when I have picked up pellets containing marine debris at Scarisbrick have been after high winds; when there is no perceptible wind the foraging range is shortened and the birds feed off the more local places.

The movements of breeding herons are of necessity limited by the needs of the broods, and although no ties restrict the movements of non-nesting birds, they too are prone to stay about one place during spring and summer, and many spend their days and nights as hangers-on about the colonies. There is no general migration but usually from two weeks after finally leaving the nests the young begin their dispersal, in the course of which individuals cover considerable distances; they may wander singly or in parties, having neither set direction nor fixed distance to travel. Some in fact do not travel at all, for they may be found at any season about certain estuaries close by the heronries.

The primary function of this dispersal is to ensure good feeding, the distance over which it extends depending on such factors as competition, weather and topography. Where foraging is good near the colony there is no inducement to wander far afield. A high proportion of the herons ringed in Cumberland are recovered in the same county, which is rich beyond the average in lakes and streams and has a convenient open seaboard against the most severe weather. By contrast Staffordshire does not offer such a wealth of feeding grounds and more widespread wanderings are the natural result.

Proof of the heron's ability to find good foraging quickly has been made evident in times of drought. Near my home in Lancashire are a number of reservoirs stocked with trout and carrying large numbers of perch which, as is usual when they throng in such waters, seldom run to any size and move in immense shoals. An occasional heron may be seen at any time but each summer, after

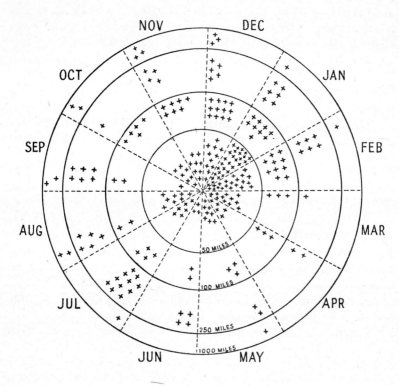

FIG. 6

Distance of dispersal from heronries in relation to the time of year

a prolonged spell of dry weather, new shallows are formed; it is astonishing how quickly the herons discover this state of affairs and up to a dozen may descend there, which in my part of the country is a considerable concentration . One September I visited another local reservoir where the water had receded, exposing an area of mud, already showing a carpet of vegetation, with small pools glistening here and there. Herons seemed to be hunting everywhere and when they flew several cormorants bore them company. This water, which lay hard by a high road linking two great cities, held the largest concourse of herons I have ever seen in such a place.

The Late E. L. Turner remarked how "between July and February many rove further afield and resort to the marshland dykes, tidal estuaries, and the seashore, mainly in search of food. These roving bands may consist of twos and threes, and during July and August from thirty to sixty may be seen together in the vicinity of Hickling Broad." Such concentrations of feeding herons on waters particularly attractive to them show that the birds are less unsociable outside the breeding season than is generally supposed. Birds hatched in Britain gradually disperse, but a promising feeding place will halt them. Indeed, the presence of such a place may cause an habitual local movement which may affect one individual or several; it may cause a concentration and may even cause some few birds to become sedentary for a time.

The Bela at Milnthorpe provides ideal fishing for birds from Dallam Tower and whenever I see a heron standing there I assume it to be from that colony. When near Southport in winter I see a heron get up from an eel-filled dyke behind the town it seems a reasonable supposition that it is from one of the two local heronries. This suggests that herons sometimes are sedentary. J. W. Seigne tells me that in Ireland big heronries situated beside a river have their tenants throughout the year and that birds may be seen perching close by the nests during any part of the night when they are not away fishing. Clearly not all British herons share in the post-fledging dispersal.

In spite of a tendency to linger near an especially well-favoured heronry, most herons undoubtedly undertake some movement.

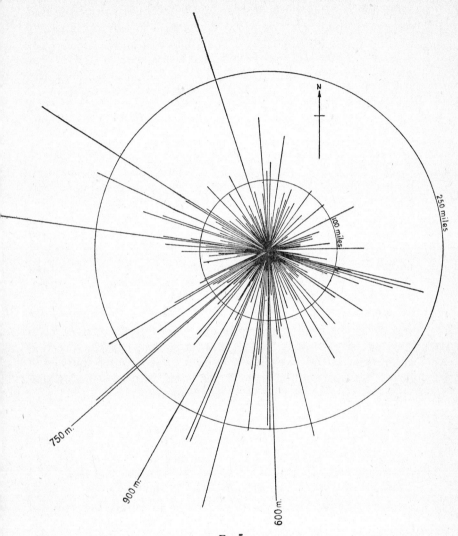

FIG. 7
Angle of dispersal from place of origin in Britain

Long before ringing was practised in Britain it was suspected that there was some trans-oceanic movement. Thompson, an early writer on Irish birds, made mention of an autumnal crossing from Scotland. T. H. Nelson remarked that he had frequently seen near the Yorkshire coast herons freshly arrived from the continent, and that he had " annually watched the birds crossing the sea from the east." G. B. Ticehurst has also published notes concerning herons he has seen on ten occasions migrating to and from the Suffolk coast.

More recently a great deal of information has been collected concerning the movements of herons, a large number having been ringed in Britain and many other European countries. The earliest definite record of any ringed bird was a heron captured in Germany in 1710, which bore metal rings on its legs affixed several years previously in Turkey. In Britain alone no fewer than 2,278 nestlings were ringed between 1909 and the end of 1945, while to the same date 284, or 12.7 per cent, had been recovered. This high percentage of recoveries has only been exceeded in this country in certain ducks, hawks and the cormorant.

An analysis of these recoveries, noting time of year, distance and direction from place of origin, confirms the fact of post-fledging dispersal (figs. 6 & 7), and shows, too, that the direction of dispersal extends over 360 degrees. Of 247 nestlings hatched in British heronries 17 birds, or 7 per cent, were recovered where ringed, while the remainder were dispersed :—

N to W .. .. .. 75 birds.
W to S .. .. .. 58 birds.
S to E .. .. .. 58 birds.
E to N .. .. .. 39 birds.

It is noteworthy that from the place of origin 114 had flown in a northerly direction and 116 southerly. Of those moving southerly the same number had taken an easterly as a westerly bias, while of the birds that went north almost twice as many inclined to the west as to the east. An example of this radial wandering may be seen when we find that nestlings marked at a heronry at Henley-on-Thames have been found, before the following nesting season, in the counties of Berkshire, Buckingham, Oxford, Warwick,

Somerset, Stafford and Lincoln. Of the nestlings ringed in Cumberland more than half have been retaken in the same county, while others have wandered to Scotland, I. of Man and Wales. Birds hatched in Staffordshire have been recovered in Cheshire, Lancashire, Yorkshire, Shropshire, Derbyshire, Northamptonshire, Lincolnshire, Gloucestershire and Radnorshire, which is probably sufficient to show that their wanderings are not controlled by any directional impulse. Later I shall show how continental herons engage in a similar dispersal, although in their case a directional impulse emerges later in the year which changes the entire pattern of the movement and has no counterpart in Britain.

Having noticed the direction of this dispersal we also find that the distance flown varies within very wide limits. The 247 recoveries already analysed to obtain a dispersal angle provide the following table.

Distance from place of origin				number of birds	Percentage
0— 20 miles	..	..	..	78	32
20— 50 miles	..	..	..	46	18
50— 100 miles	..	..	..	61	25
100— 250 miles	..	..	..	49	20
250— 500 miles	..	..	..	10	4
500—1000 miles	..	..	..	3	1

Half of the birds were retaken within 50 miles of their place of origin and three quarters within 100 miles. Only 5 per cent had travelled over 250 miles while only three individuals had exceeded 500 miles from the heronry; those three, one to the south of France and two to Spain, had flown 600, 750 and 900 miles respectively. By British standards these are very long flights indeed, but much greater distances are flown by herons of continental origin.

On relating distance to direction we find that of sixteen birds which had flown 250 miles or farther from their starting point, O had taken a course within 45 degrees of NE, 4 within 45 degrees of NW, 2 within 45 degrees of SE, and 10 within 45 degrees of SW.

These facts may suggest a similarity to the movements of European herons, which later in the year become directional, especially when it is noticed that all the distant recoveries of British herons were made in deep winter. The next table shows the relation between distance and time.

Distance (in miles) of recoveries from point of origin						Month							
	1	2	3	4	5	6	7	8	9	10	11	12	Total
0— 50 ..	28	20	11	5	8	3	6	8	1	7	8	11	116
50— 100 ..	9	10	3	3	3	2	4	2	2	5	7	12	62
100— 250 ..	6	6	1	2	2	4	11	5	6	1	4	5	53
250—1000 ..	1	1	—	—	1	—	1	2	2	2	3	3	16
Total	44	37	15	10	14	9	22	17	11	15	22	31	247

Too much significance should not be attached to the fact that almost half the recoveries were made during the months of December, January and February, for that period covers the hardest weather and an unduly high casualty rate. It is enlightening to read the table month by month, comparing each figure as a percentage of the monthly total; it then clearly shows a developing concentration towards the heronries, which reaches a peak in January. There are still many birds far from their place of origin in February, but by March, April and May the number of these distant recoveries is at a minimum. In June there is an increase and in July a very large increase, for by that time the young birds—not yet worldly-wise and especially vulnerable— are already dispersing.

Six nestlings were ringed at the heronry at Aldershaw in Sussex on 22 April 1928: before the end of June two had been recovered in Belgium, by mid-January three more were accounted for in France, while the greatest traveller of the six was recovered on 4 December 1928 at Pontivedra in Spain. All these birds had made but a single journey, the point of origin and place of recovery being exactly known. The greatest traveller from England yet recovered was a nestling marked at Henley-on-Thames on 29 April 1928 and recorded at Daimiel, in Central Spain, on 16 November 1933. That bird had made five other annual journeys in the interim and

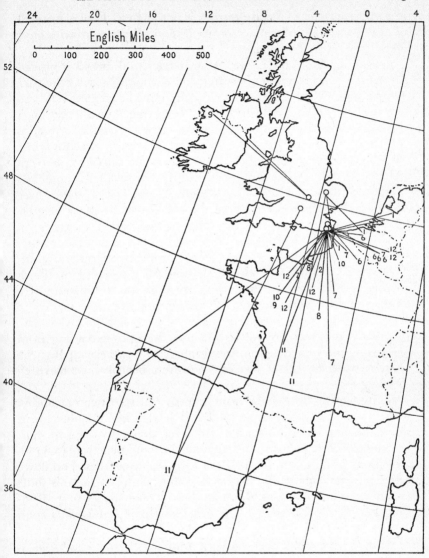

FIG. 8

Movements of British-hatched herons to continental Europe. (Numerals denote month of recovery)

the starting point of its last journey is not known. I have assumed
that it started from its place of origin and all the recoveries have
been treated in that manner.

That the English Channel is no barrier to dispersal is proved
by the large number of herons ringed in Kent and Sussex which are
recovered in Northern France and Belgium. The crossing holds no
terrors even for young birds, two nestlings ringed on 19 May 1934
having arrived in Belgium and France within a couple of months
of leaving the nest. The one recovered in France was shot while
fishing at a carp pond, only 29 days after being ringed at the High
Alstow heronry in North Kent; with it were two herons hatched
earlier in the same year at Aldershaw. The fact of these three
young birds having been shot at the same time and place suggests
that they were travelling together, furthermore it suggests an
association of birds from two different origins, which fact I shall
put forward to explain why some European migrants are recovered away from the normal stream. All the herons of British
origin so far recovered in Europe are from heronries south of a
line from the Severn to the Wash and, even if their journeys cover
the direct route, in no case is a long sea crossing involved. The
places of recovery are all in Western Europe, extending from
Holland, through Belgium and France, to Southern Spain; no
heron of British origin has yet, however, been known to reach
Africa.

Immigrants to Britain from Europe fall into two categories.
There have been many from the Pas-de-Calais and Flanders areas,
these being part of a dispersal which has generally stopped short
at our southern counties, although one bird did penetrate to South
Wales and another to the south of Eire; many of these had flown
from districts our native herons had flown into, so there is some
exchange of populations although there is no evidence of it affecting breeding populations. The other group of immigrants com-
prises birds from Norway and Sweden, Denmark, Germany and
Holland. There have been a large number of recoveries of birds
from these sources and the areas they have visited extend from
Shetland to the Channel Islands and include the whole of Britain,
penetrating westwards to the Hebrides, Ulster and Eire. In this

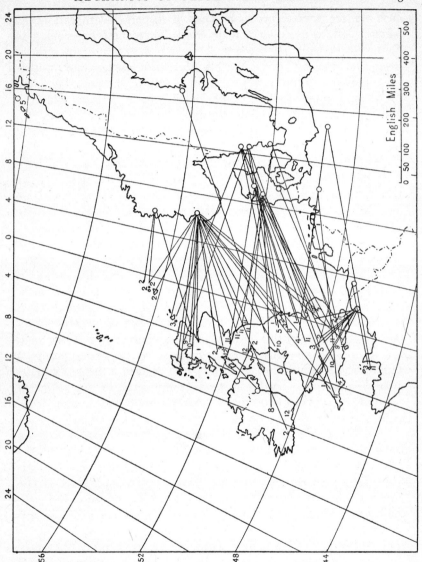

FIG. 9

Herons hatched in continental Europe recovered in Britain. Based on data
to 1945.   Numerals denote month of recovery)

case we see something more than a dispersal—an undoubted westerly migration over a wide front. Three nestlings ringed in Denmark in May 1911 were all recovered within eight months from the Firth of Forth, Norfolk and Middlesex, while another from the same country was taken in Wiltshire. The birds affected by this movement had accomplished a long sea journey which, it is interesting to note, would normally be made against the prevailing airstream. There is no reverse movement of British-hatched herons to these more northerly regions.

Although the average temperature of the coldest month (February) in Britain may in some years be 19-20°F, we do not habitually have long periods below freezing point; for this reason there is no necessity for British hatched herons to migrate, dispersal usually sufficing to bring them to accessible food: only in winters of exceptional severity is the mortality rate unduly high. The weather in continental Europe is entirely different; Copenhagen may expect 10° of frost for three months of the year, for two months Leningrad is 10°F colder than Copenhagen, while Moscow has five months of continuous frost. Herons could not survive in such climates and a complete migration is the result. Although there must be a correlation between the movements of isotherms and of the birds it is not possible to draw isochronal lines, by connecting points of simultaneous movement, as the pattern made by the movements of herons in continental Europe is complicated in that different populations succeed each other in overlapping waves, some individuals tending to become sedentary wherever the climate allows.

Soon after fledging in their continental heronries the young birds disperse, exactly as in Britain. They will not disperse northwards across the Baltic and a mountain range may be a barrier, but there is very clearly at this early stage no directional trend, the angle of dispersal being decided by local topography and ecological necessity. From the nature of such a dispersal it is obvious that a proportion of the birds will find themselves somewhere along their autumn migration line, while others are ranging elsewhere in every direction within the dispersal angle. When the real migration starts the herons dispersed in the final direction will be the vanguard. By September the true migration has developed

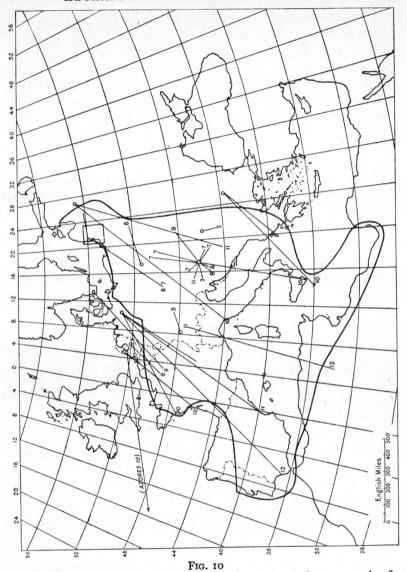

FIG. 10

Heron migrations in continental Europe. (Numerals denote month of
recovery; bounding line includes 'normal living-space'; although occasional
flights over the Sahara are referred to in the text)

to a stronger degree while in deep winter all the birds which in northern Europe may have ranged around the compass, have so ordered their flights that the dispersal angle has contracted to cover a movement on a broad front to the south-west and south.

In this directional flight most birds of north European origin overtake and pass those of more southerly origin; moreover the movement starts earlier in higher latitudes. Up to 1939 no less than 30 herons hatched in Germany had been recovered in Africa; of five recorded south of the Sahara four were hatched in East Prussia, while the fifth, taken in Nigeria, was of Hungarian origin. Most European herons reported from Africa have been in the north from Morocco to Tripoli.

How far the heron flies depends on various factors, topographical, ecological and meteorological. We have seen that only some one per cent of British-hatched herons wintered more than 500 miles from the heronries. Eighteen per cent of those of north German origin wintered more than 600 miles away, but only a single south German bird had travelled so far. There can be no hard and fast rule on this matter, as birds from the same heronry, even from the same nest, may not travel equal distances: for example a fledgling from central Germany had reached Spain by October, while two others from the same source were still within nine and twenty miles of the nests. In actual distance 3,500 miles is so far the known limit, but that bird was not recovered until 638 days after ringing, so that it was in its second migration. The greatest distance flown in the shortest time appears to have been achieved by a nestling hatched in East Prussia in 1935 which, by 3 November of the same year, had reached Togo, some 3,220 miles away, representing an average daily flight of 20 miles for each of the intervening 158 days. This must be approaching the limit of a heron's capabilities, for the bird was utterly exhausted and died within a day of being found.

In the course of my researches into the movements of the heron in continental Europe I have examined in detail the journeyings of more than 1,000 birds. A very large majority conform to the pattern already described. As the movement develops into a broad-front advance the birds, excepting those from the extreme north-west and the Danish Peninsula, tend to avoid the coastline, contrary to the custom of most other migrants. Various factors cause deviations from this broadly defined flight pattern: the direction of a river may cause a local movement or attract a group from the main pattern; the basin of the Danube and its system exerts a considerable influence in this way. Also, if individuals of a westerly origin meet with congeners of a more easterly origin they may travel with them, so pursuing a more easterly route than they otherwise would have done.

Twice a year a definite migration crosses the Mediterranean. It flows from Europe and probably the Near East to Africa, including the valley of the Nile, where some of the movements assume the nature of mass flights, up to 100 herons having been seen together. These trans-oceanic migrants sometimes display quite extraordinary powers of sustained flight; F. W. Headley gives evidence that they are capable of remaining on the wing for sixteen hours or more. The most astonishing trans-oceanic flight yet definitely established was that of a young heron, ringed as a nestling in June 1928 at Callantsoog on the Dutch coast, which by October of the same year had reached Pico, in the Azores, a journey of more than 1,500 miles, of which at least 1,000 were flown across the sea. One cannot exclude the possibility that this bird was weather-blown, as another from France recovered in the Cape Verde Islands may well also have been. The log of the steamer Columbus has an entry for 1 October 1930 recording that, while she was steaming over 250 miles SW of Co. Kerry, the nearest land, three herons arrived during strong east winds and settled on the ship. Such movements appear to be quite unusual.

Summary and Conclusions

The heron engages in several types of flight to fit varying circumstances. It soars to escape pursuit, and sometimes makes spectacular descents to the nest, although for the most part it travels horizontally at a moderate pace and height, propelled by a wing-beat twice each second. Soon after nesting both the young and old birds disperse in all directions to find good living conditions.

In the more equable parts of its range there is no marked directional trend, although the dispersal may bring about interchange of birds between England and Belgium and France. Dispersal likewise takes place on the continent, but at a later date the movement there becomes directional, with the more northerly populations passing those of more southerly origin. As part of this directional movement Scandinavian herons visit Britain, while many from north Germany travel as far as Africa.

CHAPTER 10

THE HERON IN HISTORY AND FOLK-LORE

IN THE CRETACEOUS PERIOD, the last sixty million years of the Age of Reptiles, in addition to some birds which where still toothed there were some already closely resembling forms which survive today. An extinct family of this period, the Scaniornithidae, showed relationship to herons and flamingos, and was not distantly related to the ancestors of ducks. At the beginning of the Age of Mammals (the Cenozoic era) definite herons and ibises were recognisable. So the heron family is at least sixty million years old: the storks, which belong to the same Order, are younger, as they did not detectably diverge from the main stock until the early Oligocene epoch, about forty million years ago. *Proherodias* from the Lower Eocene of the London Clay, is a real heron; and the genus *Ardea* is known from the Miocene of France and Germany (as well as the Pliocene of Oregon), which means that it is twenty or thirty million years old.

While herons are naturally not commonly found in cave deposits, fossilised bones have been found in caves in France, Germany, Bohemia, Hungary and the British Isles. These earliest specifically identifiable remains of *Ardea cinerea* L. are geologically very recent, dating from the Upper Pleistocene period and being about 20,000 years old. In the British Isles remains have been unearthed in Ireland from Ballycotton cave, from Edenvale, and from Newhall (top level) in Co. Clare. Unfortunately the Newhall finds could not be dated as the strata have been much disturbed by the digging of foxes and badgers. English records are from a cave at Clevedon in Somerset and from the Pin Hole Cave in Derbyshire associated with Cresswellian remains (c. 10,000 B.C.).

K

Remnants have been found in Danish kitchen-middens from Mesolithic times, Baltic Maglemosian, dated by Zeuner as 6,000-7,000 B.C.; as well as from the more recent Neolithic Age, and from the Iron Age.

Later prehistoric sites in Italy and Switzerland have been productive of records, while in this country, Arthur Bulleid discovered in 1892, in the neighbourhood of Glastonbury, the remains of an Iron Age (La Têne) lake-village, Celtic in origin and dating from 100 to 50 B.C. Excavations brought to light the remains of 60 to 70 dwellings, together with utensils, and bones of men, mammals and birds.

The avian remains included bones of cranes, swans, mallard, grebes, pelicans, a heron and a diver; of the heron, *Ardea cinerea*, there was found a portion of a skull; *Pelecanus crispus* remains, adult and juvenile, suggest that the species inhabited the West of England in considerable numbers. For another lake-dwelling record I am indebted to the Keeper of the National Museum of Ireland, who draws attention to some remains taken from a pre-tenth-century occupation at Lagore, Co. Meath.

Excavations of British and early Roman settlements near Colchester were started by the Colchester Excavation Committee in 1930. Among avian bones obtained there were two of the heron, and these could be definitely dated, as they came from a sealed pit in association with objects of a Belgic-British culture of the half century which ended at the latest in A.D. 43, in the reign of Cunobelinus (Cymbeline).

Ancient Egyptian art provides many instances of long-legged birds incidental to marsh scenes, but for the most part these cannot be described as belonging to any particular species although often to particular genera. Papyri from the tombs at Thebes sometimes show herons so carefully drawn and painted that there can be no doubt that they are representations of *Ardea cinerea*.

A vignette from the papyrus of Anhai, a lady of the college of Amen-Ra at Thebes, who died about 1100 B.C., shows a scene of lakes and islands; on a bank stand two Bennu birds, and Bennu birds are, unquestionably, Common Herons. An earlier and more detailed representation occurs in the papyrus of Hunefer, about

1370 B.C. A vignette from this papyrus depicts Hunefer kneeling at a table spread with offerings before a Bennu bird, which in the accompanying text is called the 'soul of Ra.' The appropriate two lines of a screed have been translated, "I am the Bennu Bird which is in Annu (Heliopolis), and I am the Keeper of the volume of the book of things which are and of things which are to be." As the Bennu bird of close upon 3,500 years ago, the heron was identified with the soul of Ra and, part bird part god, was reputed keeper of " the book of things which are and of things which are to be." Doubtless the Egyptians had seen herons engaged in

FIG. 11

The heron in Ancient Egyptian art (1370 B.C.).   Hunefer kneels with offerings before the Bennu Bird. *By courtesy of the Trustees of the British Museum*

their spiral flight until they disappeared from sight towards the sun, which would assuredly give them a connection with Ra. For this reason herons were included amongst the hieroglyphics and symbolic figures painted on wooden coffins (1580-1200 B.C.). Their presence there related to the soul's journey to the World of the Dead.

That the Greeks knew the heron well is evident. A gem, a two-inch oval of bluish chalcedony, beautifully carved by Dexamenos (450-440 B.C.), depicts as a miniature in relief a flying heron. The position is of a bird taking off, the neck not yet drawn back, the legs mid-way between the resting and flying attitude, and the details of the plumage exquisitely carved. It is difficult to comprehend how the Greeks came to believe, as we are assured they did by no less an authority than Aristotle in his *Historia Animalium*, that the heron "submits with reluctance to the duties of incubation, or to union of the sexes; in fact, it screams during the union, and it is said drips blood from its eyes." This last point may, however, have really referred to the change in the colour of the bill, discussed in Chapter 6.

The first pictorial representation of a heron in a printed book may be found in the third Tractatus of the *Ortus Sanitatis* of Johann Wonnecke von Caub. This book, a medical treatise, printed in Maintz in 1491, is the earliest printed book in which figures of birds are introduced, and along with bees, bats, and other real or legendary flying creatures, are collectively grouped in the *Tractatus de Avibus*. Amongst the rude woodcuts are recognisable figures of the stork, ibis and bittern. *Ardeola* and *Ardea* share a Capitulum setting forth something of their habits and mythology after Pliny and other early authors. The figure of a bird holding a fish bears some slight resemblance to a Dodo, but the Capitulum beneath the illustration leaves no room for doubt that it was intended to represent a heron. About this time the Japanese artist Motonobu (1745-1559) painted a delightfully realistic picture of a heron alighting, which is now in the collection at the Louvre.

The most entertaining description of a heron by an early writer was penned by the Right Rev. Erich Pontoppidan, Bishop of Bergen and a member of the Royal Academy of Science at Copenhagen. Concerning the heron in Norway he writes, "It is a large blue heron, a considerable Bird, whose body is like an Eagle's, the neck, bill, and legs, like those of a Stork, excepting that the feet resemble those of a Goose, and on their heads they have a tuft of feathers." This was published in English from the Danish original in 1755, and it is not strange that a bird with such a peculiar, if composite exterior, should have an interior anatomy in accord. Pontoppidan states that "the heron has only one straight gut, which distinguishes it from other birds." The Bishop continued

"that all my correspondents unanimously assure me, that a heron
may eat a snake or an eel three times over, which is hardly
swallowed before one sees the head and body pass out again from
the bird's fundament, and then immediately the bird turns about,
and swallows it a second time or a third time, before it will relin-

FIG. 12
The first picture of a heron in a printed book. From (H)Ortus
Sanitatis. 1491

quish it." The Irish, too, had an idea that small eels passed
uninjured through the intestines of a heron, so that the same eel
was swallowed several times in succession, and I have gleaned a
strange bit of folk-lore from the Faeroes, where there are those who
say that the heron has only one gut, and when he has swallowed a

fish he will stand with his hind-quarters pressed against the rocks so that his meal be not prematurely lost and the result of his fishing wasted. I have seen the same eel swallowed three times, but that was by three separate birds, and after each of the first two swallowings the eel was regurgitated and had not progressed lower than the gullet.

Much of the folk-lore and legend of the heron is based on fantastic beliefs concerning the bird's anatomy, especially the feet. Widespread amongst many country folk is the belief that the heron's nest is constructed with two holes through the bottom, through which the sitting bird can dangle its legs, like an old-time petty malefactor in the village stocks. Many believe that a heron hatches out its eggs by straddling the nest with its legs wide apart. This peculiar theory has often been retailed, and I have heard of a Hampshire keeper telling it in all seriousness. In Ireland, wrote Sir Robert Payne-Gallwey (1882), "it is a common habit for herons when on their eggs to leave their legs hanging outside."

Within my own experience I have met anglers who believe that certain oils extracted from dead herons possess properties attractive to fish, and this belief has existed for more than 200 years. In 1740 John Williamson wrote that "some anoint their bait with the marrow cut out of a heron's thigh-bone; and some use the fat and grease of a heron." Anglers were advised to smear the line with the following concoction, the receipt for which I give in Williamson's own words: "Take of Man's Fat, Cat's Fat, Heron's Fat, and the best Assa-Foetida, of each two Drams; Mummy finely powdered, two scruples; Camphire, Galbanum, and Venice Turpentine, of each one Dram; Civet, two grains; make them, all according to art, into an indifferent thin ointment, with the chymical oils Lavender, Annise and Camomile, of each an equal quantity. This ointment, which for its excellency some call Unguentum Piscatorum Mirabile, prodigiously causes fish to bite. The man's Fat you may get of any surgeons who are concerned in Anatomy, and the Heron's Fat from the Poulterers in London." "Herons' bowels cut in pieces, and put into a phial and buried in horse-dung, will turn to oil in fifteen days; an ounce of

asafoetida is then mixed, when it will be the consistency of honey."
Fishing lines anointed with this mixture were said to make won-
derful catches of fish in the West of Ireland.

There are many variations of the idea that herons are in some
way attractive to fish. Pontoppidan said, "its long legs are a great
help to it to get its provisions: on these legs are a very few fine
hairs, which play softly on the water; and that motion, it is said,
entices the fish, who are not aware of the devouring beak above."
Isaac Walton wrote, "some affirm, that any bait anointed with the
marrow of the thigh-bone of a heron, is a great temptation to any
fish," but unfortunately for that theory there is no marrow in a
heron's thigh-bone. An Anglican Bishop, Edward Stanley, advanced another idea: "Our Common Heron has on its breast a
considerable space devoid of feathers, filled up by tufts of down,
to which adheres a sort of clammy oily substance. It is not therefore unlikely that the oily matter may, either by smoothing the
water, or in some other way, enable the bird to attract, or when
attracted, to stalk its prey with greater certainty." The learned
Bishop further suggested that the heron may, like the fish-hawk
of North America, have some power to attract fish below the spot
where it is hovering.

The charm was supposed to be an oil contained in a small bag
on the body, and baits touched with a drop of it were considered
to be irresistible. As recently as 1899 H. O. Forbes wrote "It is
said by some to attract fish to the surface of steep pools by the
device of scattering shreds of fibres, small leaves, and bits of
vegetation as a bait, or even to shake its body scales over the
water," and I have been told quite seriously that a wading heron
stands motionless except that it wriggles its toes which, either
mistaken for worms or clouding the water and making the bird
less conspicuous, assist in its fishing. But the most firmly held
theory of all is that the heron's foot exudes an oil or a scent which
brings the fish within striking distance. So convinced are the
fisher folk of the Faeroes of the magical properties of a heron's
foot, that they carry one in their pockets, as a talisman to ensure
success in fishing.

Determined to test some of these superstitions, I prepared an extract from a heron's foot and a similar extract from the foot of a domestic fowl. The two preparations were absorbed into plaster blocks, and together with a third block without any impregnation were quietly dropped into a large tank containing a collection of roach, rudd and dace. The reactions of the fish were observed by Alfred Hazelwood, Deputy Curator of the Bolton Corporation Museums and Aquaria, whose co-operation made the experiment possible, and by my wife and myself. At no time was there a greater concentration of fish round the heron block than around either of the others, and after a few minutes, their curiosity satisfied, all the fish completely ignored all the blocks. Ample time was given to allow for the diffusion of any attractive principle; the experiment proved that no such principle existed and the decoction Unguentum Piscatorum Mirabile had no more power than other elixirs and witches' brews of the middle ages.   In conclusion a ball of food—nothing more mysterious than a pudding of oatmeal—was dropped surreptitiously into the tank. Within a few minutes every fish had crowded round it, pushing it and eating the fragments as the ball disintegrated. It was interesting to note that, whereas the fowl extract contained a considerable amount of fat, the heron extract was practically clear and free from fat globules.

In the latter part of the nineteenth century heron fat was considered to be of some medicinal value. We are told that the fat of a heron killed at the full of the moon was believed in the north of Ireland to be an excellent remedy for rheumatism. North of the border, in Angus, there was a popular superstition that the bird "is plump when the moon is full, and so lean at the change that it can scarcely raise itself, so that it can almost be taken with the hand." I have mentioned that a fluid, said to be contained in the bones of a heron, was considered an excellent salve, while the bird's fat was deemed a sovereign remedy for rheumatism—an idea doubtless originating from the thought that a bird living so much in wet places must be immune. The following items reflect the beliefs prevalent in 1865, for they are culled from the *Pharmacopaeia Londonensis* of that year: "The bill in powder, being drunk, causes sleep. The grease is anodyne and eases pains of the gout, helps deafness and clears the sight. It makes a good bait to catch fish with."

The last of these anatomical and physiological myths that I will dwell upon concerns the powder-downs. Until comparatively recently the function of these feathers was not understood, and the powder which they so abundantly supplied, was thought to have luminous properties to help the bird in its night fishing. That the powder has no such phosphorescence may be seen by placing a dead heron in a darkened place, but should that not suffice I would mention that living herons display no luminosity in the dark, nor have I been able to get any reflections or refractions from the powder itself.

An old belief prevalent in Norfolk was that two broods were usually reared in the same nest each spring, and an even stranger notion was prevalent amongst the country people that the second set of eggs was incubated by the young of the first brood (Stevenson, 1870). The keeper of the Fritton colony, in existence till 1869, is reported as saying "The birds lay a first clutch of eggs, which take three weeks to hatch; after about a fortnight they lay as many more, which are hatched off with the young in the nest." This myth may have arisen from the fact that herons start incubating with the first egg, with the inevitable result that eggs and young must be in the nest together.

During the last century it was commonly thought that herons, intent on fishing or catching frogs, became paralysed and incapable of flight if surprised by a person suddenly appearing on the bank above and making a great noise. H. O. Forbes described such an incident in which the bird remained apparently mesmerised for fully fifteen minutes. Perhaps my inability to reproduce this condition in a heron is because of my inability to surprise one, and I associated such stories with the old wives' tales of the times, yet quite recently I received a letter containing the following passage: " One of my brothers was on the Island of Oronsay, and one day when out with a gun and retriever he saw a heron on a marsh apparently asleep . . . eventually he got so near that his dog began to sniff its legs, and he laid his hand on the bird's back, when it flew off with a loud cry." Apparently it is possible to surprise a heron; but it may well be, as A. W. Boyd suggests, that so unwary a bird was sick.

An historical poem, "The Vows of the Heron," published by M. la Curne de Sainte Palaye about 1781, suggested that wariness was sometimes mistaken for cowardice—Robert of Artois, outlawed from Namur, found refuge at the court of Edward III whom he urged to seize the Crown of France. He visited the Palace in state and, accompanied by minstrels, took two plates each holding a roasted heron which he offered to the king, saying that these most cowardly of all birds were a suitable gift for the greatest of cowards—a ruse so successful that Edward pledged himself to enter France within a year. It is interesting to compare this poem with an extract from Folkard which shows a very different sentiment: "among our ancient customs, was one of swearing an oath upon the dead body of a heron, and whereby many a gallant knight has, in years long passed, plighted his troth to 'his ladye faire,' as the most solemn and honourable manner of assuring her of his sincerity."

Much folk-lore was common, with minor variations, to widely separated places, but sometimes certain beliefs were peculiar to a district. A superstition restricted to the Cleveland district of Yorkshire is worth repeating. There it is said that anyone having the misfortune to see dark-coloured birds, presumably crows or rooks, harass a heron until it casts up its catch, would presently suffer through some legal action. Should the harassing birds be light-coloured, as possibly gulls, any witness of the incident would suffer loss through death. Perhaps this was derived from a more widely held superstition, for the Rev. Kenneth Macaulay, who in 1758 became a missionary on St. Kilda, recorded how formerly in the Western Isles certain birds were accounted the genii of those about to die. If the feathered prophet was light-coloured the departing spirit was destined to Heaven, if otherwise he was foredoomed to the nether regions.

Nashe wrote in 1613 concerning the Plague of London that "the vulgar meniality conclude therefore that it is likely to increase, because a Hearnshaw (a whole afternoone together) sate on the top of St. Peter's Church in Cornhill." In his reminiscences

Lord Teignmouth observed : "I found the ancient Castle of Darn-away, in Moray, tottering in the estimation of superstitious neighbours who prognosticated ill in consequence of the seeming departure of the herons." Sometimes it was the presence of the heron, sometimes its absence which boded ill, but only in Mel-bancke's *Philotimus* have I found the idea that it is well to hear the voice of a heron: "To hear an heron cry when thou goest on Imbacie is a sign of speeding." Possibly, however, its equivalent is found in Bohemia where, it was said, the heron warned men lost in the marshes of danger and by means of its cries endeavoured to lead them to safety.

The belief that herons foretell rain or storms seems to have died out, but it had credence until the close of the last century. A pleasant little rhyme appeared in the *Spectator* for 1 June 1895.

> *Craiget heron near the hill*
> *Plenty water for the mill;*
> *Craiget heron to the sea,*
> *Fine weather it will be.*

In his *Georgics* Virgil associated the high flight of herons with the approach of stormy weather:

> " *notasque paludes*
> *Deserit atque altam supra volat ardea nubem.*"

Juliana Berners wrote "The heron, or hernsew, is a fowl liveth about waters, and yet she doth so abhor raine and tempests that she seeketh to avoid them by flying on high," and Thomson describing an approaching winter storm says:—

> " *Loud shrieks the soaring Hern, and with wild wing*
> *The circling sea-fowl cleave the flaky cloud.*"

To quote another old author, "herons flying up and down in the evening, as if doubtful where to rest, presage some evill weather approaching," and the Germans said, "Wenn der Fischreiher das Wasser aufpflugt holt er Wasser."

The Irish Saint Columba, when living on Iona is said to have foretold the arrival of an exhausted heron. It was picked up on the shore and cared for during three days, then, its strength restored, it is supposed to have returned to the Saint's boyhood home in Eire, whence it had come.

An old Highland story associates the heron with the supernatural. At Loch A na-caillach " there lived down below the woods an old woman, by habit and repute a witch, and one possessed of more than mortal power, which she used in a most malicious manner, spreading sickness and death among man and beast." Exorcised by the local minister she disappeared but it was evident she was hiding nearby as she still exerted her evil influence. A poacher caught sight of her one evening and she was seen and shot at by others as she passed on moonlight nights. At last a retired sergeant determined to free his neighbours from the witch; having loaded his gun with a double charge of powder, a crooked sixpence and some silver buttons, he went to the cairn where she had her habitation. With the first light of morning he fired at a shadowy figure flying towards the cairn and later he was found there, fast asleep with a fine heron shot dead beside him and his gun burst, but all were convinced that the heron was the caillach, for her evil deeds ceased with the firing of the crooked sixpence.

The next chapter is concerned with the heron as game, which will further stress how closely its history has been connected with that of man. I will end therefore by quoting a footnote from J. P. Hamilton's reminscences, recalling some superstitious ceremonies relevant to falconry in the reign of Edward the Confessor. After a hawk had been sick and was sufficiently recovered to fly again, the owner was thus admonished: "On the morrow tyde, when thou goest oute to hawkying, say, ' In the name of the Lord, the birds of heaven shall be beneath thy feet.' Also if he be hurt by the heron, say, 'The Lion of the tribe of Judah has conquered, Hallelujah.' "

CHAPTER 11

HUNTING AND EATING HERONS

FOR AT LEAST 2,000 years the heron has been hunted in various ways in Britain for sport and food. The Glastonbury lake-dwellers stalked their prey with slings, and succeeding generations of hunters have killed herons with the weapons of their age, or taken them alive to fatten for food. The laws of the land have included legislature to ensure the success of those privileged to take herons.

In medieval times the heron was closely associated with the sport of falconry. John Swan published in 1635 his *Speculum Mundi*, in which we are told that " the heron or hernshaw is a large fowle that liveth upon waters" and has a great hatred of hawks, which is duly returned. "When they fight above in the air they labour both especially for the one thing, that they may ascend and be above the other. Now if the hawk getteth the upper place he overthroweth and vanquisheth the heron with a marvellous earnest flight." If the heron rises above the hawk " then with his dung he defileth the hawk, rotting and putrifying his feathers." This quaint belief was reiterated in the *Boke of St. Albans* by that sporting prioress Juliana Berners, and a century earlier Turner had related that the heron "routs Eagles and Hawks, if they attack it suddenly, by very liquid mutings of the belly, and thereby defends itself."

The last British owner of falcons 'entered' to the heron died in 1871, and even at that date, outside Norfolk, there was apparently no suitable ground left to follow the sport. English falconers who wished to fly their casts at herons repaired to the Hawking Club ground at Loo in Holland, where a large establishment was maintained jointly by the King of Holland and the Club, the members

supporting 22 falcons and the King 22, complete with a full com-
plement of falconers and staff.

A great number of herons were taken by the Loo club hawks;
Clough Newcome, a Norfolk squire, took with a single pair of
peregrines, named Sultan and De Ruyter, partly at Loo and partly
in Norfolk, 54 herons in 1843 and 57 in 1844. Schlegel and
Wülverhorst recorded that in 1842 the 44 trained hawks maintained at Loo took 148 herons; in 1843, 40 took 200. The following
year 36 hawks accounted for 100 herons, which remained about
the annual figure until 1849, when the number of hawks had
shrunk to 14 and the herons taken increased to 128, which suggests
that the hawks had been flown more frequently than normally.
In 1852, 292 herons were taken: the average for 8 years in succession was no less than 178.

At Loo all herons taken were liberated, and few seem to have
been much worse for the combat. The hawks would release their
quarry near the ground, and renew the attack when the heron was
down, but by this time hard riding enabled the falconers to inter-
vene. They released the heron, having fixed a copper ring on its
leg bearing the date, and having taken from the bird's head the
black plumes which, set with jewels, were worn in the falconer's
cap. Apparently it was not exceptional to take a heron bearing
three or four rings, and heron-hawking as practised at Loo seems
to have been one of the least bloody of blood-sports.

In Norfolk and in Holland herons were taken as they flew to
the heronries from their feeding grounds. This limited the places
where the sport could be successfully practised, for it necessitated
a heronry situated a considerable distance from the principal
fishing place, with intervening open country providing no convenient cover for the harried birds and a terrain suitable for the
horses to gallop over. At Loo all these conditions existed: the
heronry was vast and the feeding grounds distant, which ensured
a steady procession of birds passing to and from their nests,
while for miles around the horses could gallop their best over the
heathland and holding dunes. There was neither cover for the
herons to drop into, nor water, which in many otherwise suitable
places made the sport impossible, for a hard-pressed heron readily

seeks refuge in water, in which it is more than a match for any trained hawk, its beak providing ample protection, and neither man nor dog can dislodge it.

In England there never has been an establishment anything approaching the one at Loo, but there was, until 1838, the High Ash Club. The members hawked herons under ideal conditions at Didlington in Norfolk and the closing of the club marks the end of heron hawking in this country. In Ireland many a heron was taken by hawking: both eyas (taken as nestlings) Iceland Falcons and passage peregrines having been used there, and flown at birds as they rose and not at birds in flight. In the old hawking parlance they were birds 'at siege' which, in its modern counterpart, suggests sitting game:

> *"Lo, at his siege, the heron*
> *Upon the bank of some small purling brook*
> *Observant stands, to take his scaly prize,*
> *Himself another's game."*   (SOMERVILLE)

The heron's formidable bill does not seem to have provided any protection during flight, but on the ground it is a dangerous weapon, and more than a few falcons, slow at 'making-in,' were badly stabbed. During a hawk's training it used to be the practice to try it against a heron which had been captured and rendered temporarily harmless by the wrapping and padding of its mandibles. Stories of hawks being transfixed by a heron's bill in a 'stoop' are to be taken with caution, for so far as I can find not one of them has any foundation in fact. Peregrines were most used, and although success was sometimes achieved with birds taken as nestlings and reared for the purpose, the falconers preferred adult birds, trapped and taken for use against herons, and known as 'passage falcons.' At Valkenswaard, near Eindhoven in Holland, a flourishing trade was carried on by the local professionals in trapping and supplying all manner of hawks during migration.

Such birds were that historic pair Sultan and De Ruyter. They were imported by John Pells, one time Deputy Falconer to the Duke of St. Albans. Together they brought down 111 herons in two springs, before one was lost flying at rooks in Norfolk when out with Newcombe. John Pells died at Lakenheath, Suffolk, in 1883, close by where I have seen herons nesting 60 years later in low trees surrounded by fen, as they did long before his day.

For a description of how hawks were trained for this ancient sport I can do no better than refer readers to that quaint book *The British Sportsman* by William Augustus Osbaldiston, which appeared about 1797. Alas, from his dissertation, we are left in no doubt that there was a baser side to heron hawking, as the train-herons were often rendered defenceless by having their legs broken and their bills tied up, and were thus at the mercy of the novice hawks.

In his *Accounts of the Lord High Treasurer of Scotland*, 1473-98, Thomas Dickson tells us that herons which had been struck by hawks were either released to furnish fresh sport, or kept to be used in perfecting the training of other falcons. For that purpose live herons were frequently brought to the King, as the following extracts testify:

> 1496. "Item, the last day of July, giffin to the man that brocht twa herronis to the King to mak tranys to halkis, 9s." 1497. "Item, that samyn day gevin be the Kingis command to ane man of the Lard of Dawikkis, that brocht quik herounis to the King . . . 18s.

The Authorised Version of the *Book of Deuteronomy*, Chapter XIV verse 18 clearly sets a ban on the eating of herons: " But these are they of which ye shall not eat . . . and the stork, and the heron after her kind, and the lapwing, and the bat." Nevertheless in Europe in the Middle Ages both the cross-bow and the long-bow figured as engines of destruction against the heron. Herons taken with hawks, unless wanted for train-herons, were usually liberated. According to the *Epitome of the Art of Husbandry* we have it that " the best way to take this great enemy of fish is this; having found his haunt, take three or four small Roches or Daces, and having a strong Hook with a Wire to it, to draw the Wire just withinside the skin of the Fish, beginning withoutside of the Gills, and running it to the tail, and then the fish will live for six days alive: For if the fish be dead, the Heron will not touch him. . . . Lay not your Hooks in deep water, where the Heron cannot wade to them, for if you do they will lie long enough before you see any effects for your pains. Colour your Line of a dark green, for the Heron is a very subtle bird."

For continental fowlers *Ruses Innocentes* gave similar instructions for capturing both this bird and the bittern. Sometimes too, it was suggested that baiting with a frog would be most successful, but all accounts are unanimous as to the cautious character of the heron. To overcome this by playing on the bird's curiosity Markham advised the employment of a decoy—"making her now and then to flutter her wings." The netting of herons was practised in Egypt during the present century and may still continue, and in India decoy herons were normally employed to catch others. The *Account Book of Hurstmonceux Castle*—1643-49, contains several references to a method of taking herons by means of a hook fastened to a pole, by which the young birds were pulled down from the nests, or from the tree-tops when they were branchers. There seems little doubt that many of the herons and spoonbills included in the L'Estrange accounts for Hunstanton were taken by this means, for it provides a cheap if rather brutal method of securing the birds in their prime.

No royal banquet was complete without herons. For the Christmas feast in Dublin in 1171, Henry II provided herons amongst a multitude of other dishes (Gilbert, 1865). In the reign of Edward I, a young heron was valued at eighteen pence, while an old one was to be had for twopence less, a price, according to Folkard, higher than for any other wildfowl.

The following extracts from various household books show the extent to which these birds entered into menus of the good old days. In L'Estrange's accounts occur these lines:—

It. A hernsewe and 12 rabbits of store.
It. 2 hernsewes and 12 rabbetts of store.
Itm. A pygge and 12 hernsewes and 16 rabbets of store.
It. A fawne and 2 hernsewes and 14 rabbets of store.
It. 8 malards, a bustard, and 1 hernsewes, killed wt ye crosbowe.

From the Lord North accounts referring to the Kirtlinge festivities during the visit of Queen Elizabeth I, we learn that 28 hernshewes

L

were supplied at £4 13s. 4d. The *Northumberland Household Book* informs us that " it is ordered that Hearonsewys be bought for my Lord's own Mees, so that they be at a shilling a piece." During the reign of Edward IV, George Nevill was enthroned Archbishop of York; in Pennant's *British Zoology* is transcribed from the writings of Leland an account of the feast given on that occasion. The fare included 204 cranes, 204 bitterns, 400 herons and 200 pheasants, certainly an enormous spread for that gathering of ecclesiastics. As recently as 18 May 1812, the executors of Thomas Sutton, founder of the London Charterhouse, gave a feast in the Hall of the Stationers' Company, when amongst the joints and game roasts were included six herons.

For some time before 1272, the hucksters and dealers were charging such exorbitant prices for food that the City of London Authorities set up a tariff of provisions. The heron was valued at sixpence, while fourpence would buy a pheasant and three half-pence the best hen.

A fifteenth century bill of fare is given in verse by Barclay, in his Ecloges:

> " *What fishe is of savor swete and delicious,*
> *Rosted or sodden in swete herbes or wine,*
> *Or fried in oil, most saporous and fine—*
> *The pasties of a hart—*
> *The crane, the fessaunt, the peacocke, and curlewe,*
> *The patriche, plover, bittorn, and heronshewe,*
> *Seasoned so well in licquor redolent,*
> *That the hall is full of pleasant smell and scent.*"

King Philippe le Bel attended an elaborate feast in 1458 at Tours to mark the engagement of Gaston de Foix and Madame Magdaline of France. The meal opened with white hypocrass (a cordial made from spiced wine) and toasts, followed by capons and gammons of bacon, then an array of swans, peacocks, bustards, herons, bitterns, many other wildfowl and venison. Even in fiction there are a few better menus than this, but Rabelais included the heron in the colossal meal King Grandosier made for Gargantua. Dozens of imaginary bitterns, herons, moorhens, storks and coots had their place on that occasion. Compared with the feast of Gargantua, Scott's marriage breakfast for Cranston and the Lady Margaret sounds quite a light meal;

> "*O'er capon, heron-shew and crane,*
> *And princely peacocks gilden train,*
> *And o'er the Boar-head, garnished brave,*
> *And Cygnet from St. Mary's wave,*
> *O'er ptarmigan and venison*
> *The priest had spoke his benison.*"

It is to an unknown author, who signed his preface with the initials W.M. and dedicated his three-part work to Queen Henrietta Maria, that I am indebted for the correct terms used when referring to the various game birds, in the luxury and refinement surrounding the court of Charles I. In the third part of this book, dated 1656 and entitled *The Complete Cook*, we learn the custom was to 'rear a goose,' 'truss a chicken' and 'dismember a heron.' The heron in those days was indeed a Royal Bird and it took its place at the head of the game roasts. It was larded with "swynefat and eaten with ginger." The flesh, we are told, is hard and dark-coloured, but not so fishy as some piscivorous birds. The following lines by Alexander Neckam, foster-brother to Richard Coeur de Lion, doubtless echoed the sentiment of his time:—

> "*Judicio procerum grati solet esse saporis,*
> *Vix horum mensas gratior ornat avis.*"

Two sentences from *A Dietary of Helth,* a sixteenth century treatise by a physician, Andrew Boorde, gives the medical view on the heron as food. First we learn that " a bittern is not so hard of digestion as a heron," then that " a young heron is lighter of digestion than a crane." The following receipt is from a modern cookery book *Pot Luck.* " Before cooking it must be ascertained that no bone of the heron is broken. These bones are filled with a fishy fluid, which, if allowed to come in contact with the flesh, makes the whole bird taste of fish. This fluid, however, should be always extracted from the bones and kept in the medicine cupboard for it is excellent for applying to all sorts of cuts and cracks. The heron is first picked and flayed. Then slices are cut from the breast and

legs to make the pudding. The crust is made exactly like that of a
meat pudding and the slices of heron put in and seasoned exactly
as meat would be. The pudding is boiled for several hours according to its size." For those who prefer roast heron Rolland reminds
us in his *Faune Populaire de la France* that "le peuple prétend que
le héron a sept vesicules de fiel" and in *Le Vrai Cuisinier François,*
Brussels, 1699, instructions are given to remove these seven gall-
bladders before roasting the heron.

As the flesh of the young bird was the more highly valued,
naturally the possession of a heronry was considered no small
perquisite to a property. Willughby and Ray, writing in the middle
of the seventeenth century, inform us that "we have heronries in
England such as they have in France, however Bellonius denies it:
in which herons are so well instructed and accustomed to breed,
that the owners make yearly a good profit on the young." Still
earlier, in the year 1517, the woods belonging to an Abbot in
Somerset yielded an annual return of about a hundred young
herons. Young birds were fattened for the table in special aviaries,
or stews; one such was in existence at Naworth Castle in 1620,
and on 1 July of that year an "Extraordinary paiment" was made
to Andrew Creake "for making the room for the Hernsues 13d."
This fattening shed was intended to house seventeen young herons.
For successive days in July occur these entries—"To Mr. Heron's
man of Chipchase bringing 12 hernsues s3. d4." "My Lady
Savill's man bringing 14 gulls and 5 hernsues, s5." While for 10
August 1622, we read (inter alia) of the purchase of a knife to cut
the gull's meat 2d.

The value set on its flesh was a temptation to destroy the heron
long before fishing interests became a threat. Forest and game
laws appear to have been strictly enforced, rights to take herons
by hawking or with the long-bow belonging to none but Freemen.
By *Statute 19 of Henry 7 Cap 11* it was laid down that "none shall take
an old Heron, except out of his own Ground, in Pain of 6s. 8d.
Nor a young Heron in Pain of 10s for which Forfeitures every man
that will, may sue by Action of Debt, or otherwise," and the
offenders could be committed to prison until the forfeitures were
satisfied. By *Statute 25 of Henry 8 Cap 11* it was further ordained that

"none shall destroy or take away the Eggs of any Wild-Fowl, in Pain to Forfeit for every Egg of a Crane or Bustard, so taken or destroyed 20d, of a Bittern, Heron, or Shoveland 8d, and of a Mallard, Seal, and other Wild-Fowl 1d, to be divided betwixt the King and the Prosecutor." Nor was it until the Game Act of George IV that these statutes were repealed.

Even more severe was Scottish Law, for during the reign of James IV, in 1493, an act was passed by the Scottish Parliament "anent the Distroying of Heron sewes." In 1567 the Act was renewed against all such as shoot with "culveringis, crosbow, or handbow ony time at Dae, Rae, Hart, Hind, Hair, Cunning, Dow, Herron, or foule of river," the penalties being that they "sall foir-fault and tyne their haill moveable gudis," and "gif the committer of the cryme be ane vagabound, not havand gudis, that the judge, quhom befoir he is convict, keip and hauld him in prison for the space of fourty dayis. And that for the first fault. And for the nixt fault, to cut off his richt hand."

Before the arrival of the Danes in Ireland in A.D. 795, Celtic law prevailed under the jurisdiction of the Brehons who had held courts from prehistoric times, settling disputes arising over such matters as swarming bees and straying domestic animals, in which category pet herons were specified along with deer, wolves, hawks and foxes. When hunger demanded the pet herons would, it seems likely, go to the pot. Thus for at least twelve centuries the heron has been regarded as desirable for sport and banquet, and for most of that time its welfare has been legally safeguarded.

Herons are no longer eaten in Britain. These birds were never the usual fare of the common man, but the perquisite of the "big house" and ranked as game. They were eaten during the centuries when "My Lord" filled his larder from his own estates and even then herons were chiefly served as a ceremonial dish at banquets and at "principal feasts." Changes in farming brought about changes in diet, commerce introduced different foods, and the taste for herons, as for many other wildfowl, gradually diminished until, by the middle of the nineteenth century, they had completely disappeared from the menus, being replaced by domestic poultry, which had become the most popular table-fowl.

CHAPTER 12

POSTSCRIPT

In 1950 a pair of herons left Dam Wood and nested in a younger beech plantation on the estate. That may well have been the beginning of the end of the Dam Wood heronry, for in 1953 all but four pairs had moved from the old site to the new. High gales during 1952-53 uprooted many birches and conifers, and this together with increasing disturbance, speeded the removal. Although such movements of heron populations are always taking place they do not affect the numerical strength of the species, for in 1928 Nicholson found no evidence indicating a decline in the number of herons in England and Wales over the previous two or three hundred years, nor is there any reason to believe that any substantial change has taken place since then.

Various causes bring about this shifting of populations. Import restrictions on foreign timber during two wars hastened felling operations, which initiated biotic changes. Experience in Denmark and in Cumberland shows that these have reduced the size of heronries but increased their number. Present-day afforestation stands are so closely planted that they are quite unsuited to the requirements of herons.

No British heronry now exceeds 100 nests and generally in view of the changing conditions they may be expected to be smaller than at present. The average number of nests in heronries in England and Wales is 15, in Wales alone 7. More than half contain ten nests or fewer, while more than a quarter have five or under.

Amongst suggested reasons for the disappearance of heronries listed as extinct in 1928, water-pollution finds no place, but in the first post-war heron census taken in Holland it was given as a very real contributing factor to the decrease since the German occupation. In the Scottish Highlands salmon-spawning is disturbed by pollution from industrial wastes and long reaches of some English rivers have been rendered void of all life, save a few leeches, while tidal pollution has been particularly bad. Such spoiling of a chief feeding place adjacent to a heronry is bound to have repercussions on the herons. Whether depopulation is permanent will depend on whether the pollution continues.

Another factor which will have increasing relevance in the future is disturbance. I have shown that breeding herons need a certain amount of privacy, but no matter how close to a busy place a heronry may be, if the wood itself is secluded the birds will remain in occupation.

It will be recalled that the heron population of Britain is, in the main, non-migratory. In a winter of exceptional severity a great number perish and this is the greatest single factor controlling the British heron population. After a winter of heavy loss it takes two years to recover. Alexander (1944) suggested that the reduction in the number of pairs was due to failure to breed rather than to death; but returns prove there is a high mortality. Lack (1946) supports the idea that in a year of lower population density the mortality rate is lowered and the balance thereby speedily restored. A series of severe winters would devastate the heron population and if every other winter were a bad one (for herons) the species would not fully recoup its losses and would eventually decline. Occasional hard winters have only a temporary lowering effect, the birds' enhanced nesting success quickly restoring any loss. That the species can survive in small breeding units is evident, since a quarter of the herons' nests in England and Wales are already in groups of no more than five. It should be remembered, too, that in Ireland, where the scattering of heronries has advanced a stage farther than in England, many pairs nest alone or a couple of pairs together. Again I would refer to Stevenson, who observed that about the year 1800 herons in the fens did not nest in colonies like rooks but scattered in single pairs through the area.

Contemporaneous with an increase in the breaking-up of estates, tree-felling, and pollution, there has been a general

reduction and sometimes complete cessation of gamekeeping, together with the transfer of sporting and riparian rights from their
hereditary owners to hotels and syndicates. While it is true that
before the wars, in Ireland, the Scottish Highlands and in parts
of England, keepering had been a depressing factor on the heron
population, the majority of keepers had little concern with herons
and often the presence of a keeper afforded them protection and
freedom from disturbance. Many a wood which by tradition was
almost sacrosanct is now Tom Tiddler's ground and the herons'
tenure more precarious than ever before. Keepering in the past
has probably been, on balance, beneficial to the heron, but the
invasion of the country by a new type of sportsman may have
results nobody can foretell.

The nesting cycle runs along formalised lines with which the
reader is already familiar, but there are still problems. Every year
many herons do not nest and the composition of this population,
what age-limits bound it and what is its sex-ratio, are unknown.
One explanation may be that the non-nesting birds are sexually
immature, but that does not explain why so many haunt the heronries at nesting time unless it is a continuation of the urge that
caused nestlings to go through the movements of nest-building.
As they do not, I believe, come to the gathering ground before
the start of operations they do not come within the formalised
breeding pattern. Another explanation could be that the sex-ratio
of the species is unbalanced: it is not peculiar to the heron that
the female is reproductively mature earlier than the male; and
if the males take longer to reach the reproductive stage there is
a strong probability that more males must be hatched to compen-
sate for a longer wastage period. There is yet a third possible explanation, namely that some of the non-breeding birds at least
have bred before, but either for lack of mates or some other cause
the normal tenor of their life cycle is interrupted. It may be that
all these factors contribute towards the non-breeding population.

I have dealt at some length with the heron's feeding habits,
and stressed that not only is it a bird of catholic tastes but also
that it will use other than its specialised method to get food. Anyone living where there happens to be a heavy infestation of moles

adjacent to a heronry would have a good chance of solving yet another mystery—how herons catch moles—for that they have developed a technique in that art is certain. Most of all there is yet opportunity for research in the still vexed problem of the effect the heron has on trout. It is over the preservation of fish that the only clash between the heron and man now occurs and it is my belief that the heron actually increases prospects for the human angler by helping to improve the stock of fish. This subject is dealt with by T. T. Macan and E. B. Worthington in *Life in Lakes and Rivers* in The New Naturalist main series, where readers may study the relationship between 'stock and crop' in the waters of these islands, Europe, America and New Zealand.

Trout-preservers, alas, have for too long regarded the heron as vermin, but perhaps a new era is dawning, with scientists from biological research stations to advise. In that era anglers may catch larger if fewer trout, while herons may be regarded in a different light, as reducing the stock but improving the crop. Very few other people are hostile to the heron and the great majority take pleasure in the sight of one standing ankle-deep in some pool, as so aptly expressed by Edward Boyd,

> *"wi a bygone dignity*
> *lak an auld dominie*
> *or a sticket*
> *minister."*

Dialect and Folk-names

THE NAME heron or hern, often with -shaw or -sew as a suffix, had, from the fifteenth century and probably earlier, many variations, which seem to owe their existence entirely to the erratic spelling of the cooks and account-keepers of those times. Thus we find in the accounts of Naworth Castle, for provisions supplied over the years 1610-22 the following words or spellings: heronshewe, hernshew, hernshow, heron-shew, hernsue, hernshue and hern.

Apart from these culinary discoveries, I have gathered together from various dictionaries, county faunas and other sources, a series of names, or variations of a name, which seem to owe their being to the vernacular of the various districts.

Norfolk	—	harn; harnsey.
Suffolk	—	harnser.
Nottingham	—	hernshaw; heronshaw; herring-sue.
Yorkshire	—	hernsew; heronseugh; heronsew; herring-sew; heron-sue; heronshaw; heronshew.
Northumberland	—	hearon-sewys.
Cheshire	—	yern; yarn; varn.
Roxburgh	—	huron.
Berwickshire	—	hurant; huran; heronsheugh.
Forfar	—	herald.

All these county variants appear to be phonetic interpretations of dialect.

Heronseugh or heronshaw is also an Old English name but concerning its derivation authorities differ. In Chaucer,

> *"I wot not tellen of his strange sewes,*
> *Ne his swans, ne his heronsewes,"*

the general supposition is that sewe has a culinary significance, hence heron-sewe may be a young and tender heron, fit to be eaten. 'Not to know a hawk from a heronshaw' was an old proverb owing its origin to the diversion of falconry: in a corrupted form Hamlet told Guildenstern, "I know a hawk from a handsaw."

There is also a considerable collection of popular names of an entirely different order. Some are familiar names which may be known over a wide or a restricted area, others are descriptive of the bird's legs, neck or voice. The following list may not be exhaustive but it does supply examples of each of these origins.

Sussex	—	Jack Hern; Jack Heron.
Suffolk	—	Frank.
Essex	—	Frank (from the call).
Midlands	—	Moll Hern.
Cheshire	—	Longnix; Lung-necked yern.
Lancashire	—	Jemmy Lang-legs; Jammy Lang-neck; John Crane; Frank; Johnny Gant; Jammy.
Yorkshire	—	Long-neck.
North	—	Jenny Crow (Swainson).
Pembroke	—	Longie Crane.
Kirkudbright	—	Jenny Heron.
Berwickshire	—	Lang-necket Haaran.
Dumfriesshire	—	Jenny Hern; Long-necky heron; Long necky; Craigie Crane.
Stirlingshire	—	Frank; Craigie Heron; Craiget Heron; (according to Swainson craig-throat and these names are of anatomical derivation. There is a Gael word craig meaning a rock and the name might well be derived from the bird's habit of perching on rocks).
Perthshire	—	Tammie Herl.
North Scotland	—	Craigie Heron.
Shetland	—	Haigrie; Hegrie; Hegril's Skip; Skip Hegrie.
Ireland	—	Long-necked Heron; Crane; Coreisk (Watters, archaic).
Wales	—	Crëyr glâs (in North Wales, literally blue screamer); Cregyr and Crechydd (both denoting a screamer).
Gaelic names	—	Corra ghribheach; Corraghritheach; Corra-ghriodhach; Corra Riatach. (corra-heron, grith-scream. Early Irish). (A Gaelic proverb translated as " a heron on the shore " implies a likely sight and signifies nothing unusual.
Isle-of-Man	—	Coayr; Coayr-ny-hastan (crane-of-the-eel); Coayr glas (grey crane).

Herons have often from earliest times been miscalled cranes; numerous place-names, such as Cranbrook, owe their being to the one-time presence of a heronry. I have met with the name ' Crane ' from Cornwall to Cumberland, while in Scotland and Ireland that term is still in common usage for the heron.

In continental Europe the following are the names in ordinary usage in the respective languages of the various peoples. Excepting the German and Danish forms of ' Fish Heron ' there is no adjective used to describe this bird in all the tongues of Europe which has not its counterpart in English. There are Common Herons, Blue-, Grey-, Ash-coloured and Crested Herons and also a Russian equivalent of Heronshaw.

Czech	—	Volavka popelava	—	Common Heron
Danish	—	Fiskeheejre; Graa-hejre	—	Fish or Grey Heron.
Dutch	—	Blauwe reiger	—	Blue Heron
Finnish	—	Harmaa haikara	—	Grey Heron
French	—	Héron cendré; Héron huppé	—	Ashen or Crested H.
German	—	Fischreiher	—	Fish Heron
Hungarian	—	Szurka gém	—	Grey Heron
Icelandic	—	Gráhegri	—	Grey Heron.
Italian	—	Airone cenerino	—	Ashen Heron.
Norwegian	—	Heire	—	Heron
Polish	—	Czapla siwa	—	Grey Heron.
Portuguese	—	Garca real	—	True Heron
Russian	—	Cepár nanar	—	Grey Heron
Spanish	—	Garza real	—	True Heron
Swedish	—	Grá hager	—	Grey Heron
Turkish	—	Balikçi kusu	—	Fisherman Bird

Among bordering non-European languages we have, in

Arabic	—	Bon-auk.
Moorish	—	Aishoush; Bon-auk.
Maltese	—	Russet-griz; Russet-irmiedi.

From earliest times the heron has been familiar in most parts of Africa. The ancient Egyptians knew it as the Bennu Bird; today its name is spoken in many tongues from Tunisia to the Cape. In Tunisia the French name is used; the natives of Lake Nyasa use the name *khogwe*. In South Africa the equivalent of the Dutch name prevails in the form *blou-reier,* while certain tribal names have been given by Roberts such as *kokolofitoe* in the Sesutu, and *u-Ndofu, u-Cofuza* and *u-Kwalimanze* in use by the Xhosa tribes. Among the languages of West Africa we find *sarr-ku* in Mandingo, *zalbe* in Hausa, *Ako* in Yoruba and *malakote lusa* in Kenya.

Farther east the heron is known as *ukar* in Turki; *kabud, nari, sain* and *anjan* in Hindustani; *sada-kanka* in Bengali; *saa* or *bagalo-kabaro* in Sind; in Behar it is the *khyra;* in Telugu *narraina-pachi;* in Tamil *narayan, narai* and *pambo-narai* (snake-crane)are used. In Cingalese either *indura-koka* or *kalapua-karawal-koka* may be in use. In the Malayan Peninsula, in addition to the Tamil forms are the Malay words *puchong* (more usual for the smaller herons) and *Burong seriap* which, literally translated as the grey sea-heron, is used quite indiscriminately for the common or dusky-grey heron. The Japanese familiar name is *aosagi*.

References to Appendix 1, fully listed in the Bibliography.
Jørgensen and Blackburne (1941), Dwelly (1941), Roberts (1940), Swainson (1885), Swann (1913), Watters (1853).

A Note on the Physiological Basis for Seasonal and Temporary Colour-changes in the Heron's Feet and Bill

THE PHENOMENA of the colour-changes of featherless parts of the heron, referred to in chapter 6, appear to be due to two entirely different processes.

SEASONAL COLOUR-CHANGES

A gradually deepening suffusion of the bill and feet is not peculiar to this species but is common to several herons and heron-like birds, and appears to be a visible sign of a chain of physiological changes which result in procreation. The changes result from a more active metabolism consequent upon lengthening daylight and a more adequate food-supply which not only brings about maturity of the sex-organs but produces a surplus of endocrine secretions which, in certain species of birds, may change the colour of feathers (by subtractive change or other means—Staples, 1949), or in others bring about colour-changes in the keratinised structures such as the bill and feet.

The carotenoid pigments, responsible for the yellow and red colour in these parts of the heron, are a group of closely-allied unstable chemical compounds. The importance of B-carotene in the economy of life is due to the fact that it can be converted into vitamin A by the animal. It has been shown that rats were able to repair vitamin A deficiency when their diet was supplemented by carotene (Moore, 1929). The presence of carotene in the animal presumably bears some relationship to food and can be ingested from food; thus flamingos in the London Zoo are kept in excellent condition so long as they have access to a pond stocked with small crustacea, a rich source of carotene, without which they soon lose their rosy colouring.

As I see it herons, to a lesser or greater degree, take in increased amounts of foods from which they can obtain B-carotene before their breeding season starts, some being converted to vitamin A, some remaining as carotenoids. The surplus carotenoids accumulate and are carried, in fat, to the bill and feet. Later in the spring the bird's metabolism adjusts itself, the accumulation stops and is finally dispersed or absorbed.

TEMPORARY COLOUR-CHANGES

Although there are many instances of quickly changing colour in reptiles and fish, such changes are not common in birds. The display of the male ostrich supplies a splendid example as the front of its legs and neck become for a moment a fiery red; the bill and feet of herons appear to undergo comparable changes, though to a less spectacular degree, when the birds collect on their standing ground.

What we see in this ostrich display is nothing more than an exaggerated 'blush' and similarly the fleeting colour changes in the heron's bill and feet seem to be due to the dilation of blood-vessels seen through a thin layer of transparent keratin.

See references in the Bibliography (p. oo).
Moore (1929) (1930), Staples (1949), Völker (1936).

BIBLIOGRAPHY

ALEXANDER, H. G. (1927). A List of Birds observed in Latium, Italy, between June 1911 and February 1916. *Ibis*, (12), *3:* 659-91 (p. 682).

ALEXANDER, W. B. (1940-1950). The Index of Heron Population. *A publication of the British Trust for Ornithology. Brit. Birds, 33:* 304; *34:* 189; *35:* 210; *36:* 206; *37:* 205; *38:* 232; *39:* 201; *40:* 204; *41:* 146; *42:* 81; *43:* 78.

ANDREWS, C. W. (1899). On Some Remains of Birds from the Lake-dwellings of Glastonbury, Somerset. *Ibis*, (7), *5:* 351-58.

ARCHER, SIR G. and GODMAN, EVA. M. (1937). The Birds of British Somaliland and the Gulf of Aden. London, Gurney & Jackson. *1:* 41.

ARISTOTLE. Historia Animalium, book 9, p. 1

ARMSTRONG, E. A. (1942). Bird Display. Cambridge, University Press, 7, 17, 19, 27, 29, 34, 112, 114, 121, 142, 181, 223, 253.—(1949). Diversionary Display. *Ibis, 91:* 93.

ASHBY, C. B. and RECORDS COMMITTEE OF THE LONDON NAT. HIST. SOC. (1949). Birds in the London Area 1948. *London Bird Rep. 13:* 17-18.

BAHR, P. H. (1907). A study of the Home Life of the Osprey. *Brit. Birds, 1:* 17-22 (18).

BANNERMAN, D. A. (1919). Birds of the Canary Islands, *Ibis*, (11), *1:* 715.—(1930). The Birds of Tropical West Africa. London, Crown Agents for the Colonies. Vol. 1.

BATE, D. M. A. (1934). On the Domestic Fowl in Pre-Roman Britain. *Ibis*, (13), *4:* 391.

BEDFORD, DUKE OF (1944). Heron alighting on water. *Brit. Birds, 38:* 335.

BEETHAM, B. (1910). The Home-Life of the Spoonbill, the Stork and some Herons. London, Witherby. 46.

BELCHER, C. F. (1930). The Birds of Nyasaland. London, Crosby Lockwood.

BELL, A. (1915). Pleistocene and Later Bird Fauna of Great Britain and Ireland. *Zoologist*, (4), *19:* 401-12 (406).

BERNERS, JULIANA. (1881). The Boke of St. Albans. Reproduced in facsimile. London, Elliot Stock. (first ed. 1486).

BERTRAM, W. R. (1904). Ground Nesting of Herons in Lanarkshire. *Field* 15 Oct. 691.

BIDWELL, E. (1907). *Ardea cinerea* nesting in Kew Gardens. *Bull. Brit. Orn. Cl. 19:* 86.

BIRD, C. G. (1935). A visit to the Cyclades. *Ibis*, (13), *5:* 336-55 (351).

BLAKE-KNOX, H. (1866). Ornithological notes from Wexford. *Zoologist*, (2), *1:* 95.—(1868). Ornithological notes from County Dublin. *Zoologist*, (2), *3:* 1409-10.

BLEZARD, E., GARNETT, M., GRAHAM, R. and JOHNSTON, T. L. (1943). *In* The Birds of Lakeland. *Trans. Carlisle Nat. Hist. Soc. 6:* 80-81.

BOLAM, G. (1912). Birds of Northumberland and the Eastern Counties. Alnwick, Blair. 325.—(1913). Wild Life in Wales. London, Palmar. 202.

BOLT, A. W. (1948). Ravens nesting in a heronry. *Brit. Birds, 41:* 115.

BOORDE, ANDREW. (1870). A Dyetary of Helth. London, Early English Text Soc. 270. (first ed. 1542).

BOURGOYNE, J. (1945). Une Colonie de Hérons cendrés dans le Finistère. *Oiseau, 14:* 195-96.

BOYD, A. W. (1944). Herons Swimming. *Brit. Birds, 38:* 216-17.—(1946). The Country Diary of a Cheshire Man. London, Collins. p. 270.

BRAAKSMA, S., BRUYNS, M. F. M. and BROUWER, G. A. (1950). Overzicht van de broedkolonies van de Blauwe Reiger, *Ardea cinerea* L., in Nederland in 1949. Leiden, Brill. (first publ. *Ardea, 38:* 136-62).

BROUWER, G. A. (1926). De Sterkte der Nederlandsche Blauwe Reigerkolonies in 1925. *Ardea (Bibl.)*—and JUNGE, G. C. A. (1943). Waarnemingen van broedvogels en trekvogels in 1942; 1. Broedvogels 1942, *Ardea, 32:* 193-95.

BROWN, R. H. (1927). Field notes from Lakeland. *Brit. Birds, 21:* 114-16.

BUDGE, E. A. W. (1899). The Book of the Dead. London, Brit. Mus.

BURTT, E. B. (1944). Heron and Rat. *Trans. Lincs. Nat. Union, 1944:* 53-54.

BUTURLIN, S. A. (1906). On Birds collected in Transcaucasia. *Ibis*, (8), *6:* 409.

CARR-LEWTY, R. A. (1946). Aviation and ornithology in Lakeland. *Trans. Carlisle Nat. Hist. Soc. 7:* 1-28.

CHAPMAN, A. (1893). Wild Spain. London, Gurney & Jackson. 76, 81, 271-72, 381.—(1910). Unexplored Spain. London, Arnold. 41, 186-90.

CLARK, A. H. (1907). Eighteen New Species and One New Genus of Birds from Eastern Asia and the Aleutian Islands. *Proc. U. S. Nat. Mus. 32:* 467.

CLARKE, W. E. (1912). Studies in Bird Migration. London, Gurney & Jackson. *2:* 224.

CLARKE, W. J. (1907). Nesting Sites of the Common Heron. *Brit. Birds, 1:* 155-56.

COLLENETTE, C. L. (1938). A history of Richmond Park, with an account of its birds and animals. London, Sidgwick & Jackson.

COLLINGE, W. E. (1926). The Food of Some British Wild Birds. York, privately printed. 228-29.

CONGREVE, W. E. (1929). Some notes from South-Western Transylvania and the Banat of New Rumania. *Ibis*, (12), *5:* 488.

COWARD, T. A. and OLDHAM, C. (1900). The Birds of Cheshire. Manchester, Sherratt & Hughes. 149-50.

COX, A. H. M. (1925). Raven nesting in Heronry. *Brit. Birds, 19:* 149-50.

CURREY, M. M. (1939). Heronries. *Trans. Torquay Nat. Hist. Soc. 8:* 31-36.

DAHLBECK, N. (1946). The Common Heron in Sweden. *Vär Fågelvärld, 5:* 114-18.

DARLING, F. F. (1938). Birds Flocks and the Breeding Cycle. Cambridge, University Press. 20, 68-69, 108.—(1947). Natural History in the Highlands and Islands. London, Collins. 84, 186, 250.

DARWIN, C. (1871). The Descent of Man and Selection in Relation to Sex. London.

DEANE, C. D. (1935). Herons nest with ten eggs. *Irish Nat. J. 5:* 285.

DELACOUR, J. (1932). On Birds collected in Madagascar. *Ibis,* (13), *2:* 288.

DEMENTIEV, G. P. (1938). Sur la distribution géographique de certains oiseaux paléarctiques etc. *Proc. VIII Int. Orn. Congr. Oxford, 1934:* 243-59.

DESPOTT, G. (1917). Ornithology of Malta. *Ibis,* (10), *5:* 486.

DEWAR, J. M. (1909). Field notes on the "Powder-Down" of the Heron. *Brit. Birds, 2:* 285-89.

DICKSON, T. (1877). Accounts of the Lord High Treasurer of Scotland. Vol 1. A.D. 1473-98. Edinburgh, H.M. General Register House. Preface, cclii, 287, 338.

DRESSER, H. E. (1871-81). A History of the Birds of Europe. London. Vol. 6.

DWELLY, E. (1941). The Illustrated Gaelic-English Dictionary. Glasgow, McClaren. Ed. 4.

EVANS, A. H. (1935). *Birds.* London, MacMillan, Cambridge Natural History, 95 (first ed. 1899).

FISCHER, H. F. and LADIGES, J. C. (1943). Ongewoon visschen van Blauwe Reigers, "*Ardea cinerea.*" *Ardea, 32:* 280.

FISHER, C. H. (1901). Reminiscences of a Falconer. London, Nimmo.

FITTER, R. S. R. (1949). London's Birds. London, Collins. 99-100.

FLORENCE, LAURA. (1912). The Food of Birds. *Trans. Highl. Agric. Soc. Scot. 1912:* 207-208.—(1914). *Idem, 1914:* 48.

FLOWER, S. S. (1925). Duration of Life in Vertebrate Animals. *Proc. Zool. Soc. Lond. 1925:* 1397.

FOLKARD, H. C. (1859). The Wild-Fowler. London, Piper Stephenson & Spence. 194-200.

FORBES, H. O. (1899). *in* A. G. Butler's British Birds and their nests and eggs. London, Warne. *4:* 6.

FRASE, R. (1936). Der Fischreiher, *Ardea c. cinerea* L. in der Grenzmark Posen —Westpreusen und Ergebnisse Beringung. *Ringfundmitteilung der Vogelwarte Rossitten,* no. 136.

FROHAWK, F. W. (1910). Food of the Common Heron. *Brit. Birds, 4:* 153-54.

FULLERTON, J. D. (1911). The Physical Characteristics of Birds. *Table III in the First Report of the Bird Construction Committee. London, Aeronautical Soc. of G.B.*

GILBERT, H. A. (1917). Lifting Power of the Golden Eagle. *Brit. Birds, 19:* 259.

GILBERT, J. T. (1865). History of the Viceroys of Ireland. Dublin, Duffy, 28.

M

GLEGG, W. E. (1931). The Birds of L'Ile de la Camargue et la petite Camargue. *Ibis,* (13), *1:* 419-46 (p. 419).

GORDON, ISABELLA. (1947). The Mitten Crab. *Ill. London News. 4.* Oct. 384.

GOUGH, K. (1944). Some Observations on a Remarkably Coloured Heron. *Brit. Birds, 38:* 149-50.

GOUGH, T. (1877). Observations of the Herons and the Heronry at Dallam Tower. Kendal.

GRIMEGER, D. (1945). Meeuwachtig vissende Blauwe Reigers, *Ardea c cinerea* L. *Ardea, 32:* 280.

GUICHARD, K. M. (1947). Birds of the Inundation Zone on the River Niger, French Sudan. *Ibis, 89:* 450-89 (p. 461).

GURNEY, J. H. (1899). Longevity in Herons. *Ibis,* (7), *5:* 38.

HAMILTON, J. P. (1860). Reminiscences of an old Sportsman. London, Longman. *2:* 173 (footnote).

HARDY, J. (1822). Report of the Meetings of the Berwickshire Naturalists' Club for the year 1881. *Hist. Berw. Nat. Cl. 9:* 428.

HARRISON, J. M. & PATEFF, P. (1933). A Contribution to the Ornithology of Bulgaria. *Ibis,* (13), *3:* 589-611 (603).—(1937). An Ornithological Survey of Thrace, the Islands of Samothraki, Thasos, and Thasopulo in the North Aegean, and Observations in the Struma Valley and the Rhodope Mountains, Bulgaria. *Ibis,* (14), *1:* 582-625 (p. 618).

HARTERT, E. (1917). On New Sub-Species of Birds. *Bull. Brit. Orn. Cl. 38:* 6.

HARTING, J. E. (1872). British Heronries. *Zoologist,* (2), *7:* 3261-72.

HARVIE-BROWN, J. A. & BUCKLEY, T. E. (1891). A Vertebrate Fauna of the Orkney Islands. Edinburgh, Douglas. pp. 161-62.—(1892). A Vertebrate Fauna of Argyll and the Inner Hebrides. Edinburgh, Douglas. 117.

HAVERSCHMIDT, FR. (1949). The Life of the White Stork. Leiden, Brill.

HEADLEY, F. W. (1912). The Flight of Birds. London, Witherby. 50, 117-18.

HENDY, E. W. (1930). Wild Exmoor through the Year. London, Cape. 193.

HEWITT, WM. (1849). The Heronry at Coley Park, Berks. *Zoologist,* (1), *7:* 2420-21.

HEYSHAM, JOHN. (1798). A catalogue of Cumberland Animals. *In* Wm. Hutchinson's History and Antiquities of Cumberland. Carlisle. *1:* 18.

HIBBERT-WARE, A. (1940). An Investigation of the Pellets of the Common Heron (*Ardea cinerea cinerea*). *Ibis,* (14), *4:* 433-50.

HILL, M. T. (1944). Herons swimming and diving. *Brit. Birds, 38:* 136.

HILL, W. C. O. (1926). A comparative study of the pancreas. *Proc. Zool. Soc. Lond. 1926:* 607-08.

HOLSTEIN, V. (1927). Fiskehejren. Copenhagen. 7-98.

HOWARD, HILDEGARDE. (1950). Fossil Evidence of Avian Evolution. *Ibis, 92:* 1-21 (p. 9).

HUNT, O. D. (1946). Ravens nesting in a heronry. *Brit. Birds, 39:* 340.

HUXLEY, J. S. (1924). Some points in the breeding behaviour of the common heron. *Brit. Birds, 18:* 155-63—(1942). Evolution, The Modern Synthesis. London, Allen & Unwin. 151-262, 443-44.

INGRAM, C. (1926). The Birds of the Riviera. London, Witherby. 89.

IRBY, L. H. (1895). The Ornithology of the Straits of Gibraltar. London, Porter. 200.

JAMES, SIR H. E. M. (1888). The Long White Mountain or a Journey in Manchuria. London, Longmans. 274-75.

JORDAN, D. S. and KELLOGG, V. L. (1927). Evolution and Animal Life. New York, Appleton. 328.

JØRGENSEN, H. I. and BLACKBURNE, C. I. (1941). Glossarium Europae Avium. Copenhagen, Munksgaard.

JOUBERT, H. J. (1932). Interspecific relations between a S. African weaver bird and a buzzard. *Ostrich, 3:* 58-60.

JOURDAIN, F. C. R. (1912). Birds of Corsica. *Ibis,* (9) *6:* 77.—(1928). Common Heron rearing two broods. *Brit. Birds, 21:* 202.—(1939). *In* The Handbook of British Birds. London, Witherby. *3:* 129.

KENNEDY, J. N. (1921). Birds of South Russia. *Ibis,* (11), *3:* 462.

KERSHAW, J. C. (1904). Birds of the Quantung Coast. *Ibis,* (8), *4:* 247.

KEYSLER, J. G. (1760). Travels through Germany, Bohemia, Hungary, Switzerland, Italy and Lorrain. London. 3rd ed. *1:* 87.

KIRKPATRICK, C. M. (1940). Some food of the young Great Blue Herons. *Amer. Midland Nat. 24:* 594-601.

KIVIRIKKO, K. E. (1940). Suomen Selkarankaiset, vertebrata Fennica. Porvoo.

KNABE, G. (1938). Ostpreusische Fischreiherdiedlungen und der Zug Ostpreusischreiher (*Ardea cinerea*) auf Grund sechsjahriger Bestandsaufnahmen und Beringungsergebnisse nach dem stand vom 1. Oktober 1937. *Ringfundmitteilung der Vogelwarte Rossitten,* no. 147.

KNABE, G. and RINGLEBEN, H. (1938). Beringte Fischreiher (*Ardea c. cinerea* L.) aus Europe in Africa. *Schriften der Phys.-Okon Gesellschaft zu Königsberg (Pr.) 70.*

KNIGHT, C. W. R. (1925). Aristocrats of the Air. London, Williams & Norgate. 88.

KNOX, A. E. (1855). Ornithological Rambles in Sussex. London, Van Voorst. 3rd ed. 34-35.

KUHK, R. (1935). Zug und Winterquartier der mecklenburgischen Fischreiher: *Arch. Naturges. Mecklenburg, (N.F.), 10.*

KRÜGER, C. (1947). Distribution of the Common Heron (*Ardea c. cinerea* L.) in Denmark. *Dansk. Orn. Foren. Tidsskr., 40:* 216-35. (*English summary with above title*).

LACK D. (1943). Breeding Birds of Orkney. *Ibis. 85:* 9.—(1934). The Life of the Robin. London, Witherby. 29, 52, 131.—(1946). The Balance of Population in the Heron. *Brit. Birds, 39:* 204-06.

LAMBRECHT, K. (1933). Handbuch der Palaeornithologie. Berlin. 734.

LA TOUCHE, J. D. D. (1905). Birds of the Province of Fohkien, S. E. China. *Ibis,* (18), *5:* 64.

LEACH, E. P. (1937). Recovery of Marked Birds. *Brit. Birds, 31:* 117, and subsequent reports.

L'ESTRANGE (1833). The Household and Privy Purse Accounts of the L'Estranges of Hunstanton . . . 1519-78. Communicated to the Society of Antiquaries by Danl. Gurney. *Archaeologia, 25:* 411-569.

LÖHRL, H. (1938). Der Wanderungen der Fischreiher aus dem Naturschutzgebiet Reiherhalde Morstein an der Jagst. *Ver. Wurtt. Landesstelle f. Naturschutz. Stuttgart, Heft 14.*

LORENZ, K. (1937). The companion in the bird's world. *Auk, 54:* 245-73.

LØVENSKIÖLD, H. L. (1949). Handbok over Norges Fugler. Oslo, Gyldendal Norsk Forlag. *3:* 478-81.

LOWE, F. A. (1934). Days with Rarer Birds. London, Trefoil. 93.

MACAN, T. T. and WORTHINGTON, E. B. (1951). Life in Lakes and Rivers. London, Collins. 197-210.

MACAULAY, K. (1764). The History of St. Kilda. London,

MCGREGOR, P. J. C. (1906). Birds observed at Monastir, Turkey in Europe. *Ibis,* (8), *6:* 303.

MACLAREN, P. I. R. (1944). Heron Fishing in Flight. *Brit. Birds, 38:* 256.

MACPHERSON, H. A. (1847). A History of Fowling. Edinburgh, Douglas. 212-14.

MALLOCH, P. D. (1910). Life Histories and Habits of the Salmon, etc. London, Black. 180, 232.

MANSELL-PLEYDELL, J. C. (1888). Birds of Dorsetshire. London, Porter. 129.

MAXWELL, SIR HERBERT, BART. (1904). British Fresh-Water Fishes. London, Hutchinson. 297-98.

MAXWELL, W. H. (1892). Wild Sports of the West of Ireland. Glasgow, Morison. 297.

MAYR, E. (1942). Systematics and the Origin of Species. New York, Columbia University Press. 11, 19, 21-22, 120, 275, 76, 290-91.

MEINERTZHAGEN, R. (1914). Notes from Mesopotamia. *Ibis,* (10), *2:* 394.— (1927). On birds collected at high altitudes in Ladak and Sikkim. *Ibis.* (12), *3:* 613-14.—(1930). Nicoll's Birds of Egypt. London, Hugh Rees.

MELBANCKE, BRIAN. (1583). Philotimus. The Warre Betwixt Nature and Fortune. London. Aa 3.

MENZIES, W. J. M. (1925). The Salmon. Its Life Story. Edinburgh, Blackwood, 60-61.—(1948). The Common Eel and its Capture. *Scottish Home Dept. Salmon Fisheries Publ. Edinburgh, H. M. Stationery Office.* 6-7.

MITCHELL, F. S. (1892). The Birds of Lancashire. London, Gurney & Jackson. 2nd ed. 143-44.

MITCHELL, P. CHALMERS. (1911). Longevity and Relative Viability in Mammals and Birds. *Proc. Zool. Soc. Lond.* 1911: 508.

MOLINEUX, H. K. F. (1930). A Catalogue of Birds giving their Distribution in the Western Portion of the Palaearctic Region. Eastbourne, Fowler. 222-24.

MOORE, T. (1929). Vitamin A and Carotene. *Biochem. J. 23:* 803-11, 1267-72.—(1930). *Idem. 24:* 692-702.

MOORHOUSE, S. (1940). The Heronries of an Estuary. *Northw. Nat. 15:* 227.

MUNN, P. W. (1936). Further notes on the Birds of the Balearic Islands. *Ibis*, (13), *6:* 591-94 (592-93).

MURRAY, SIR T. of GLENDOOK. (1681). The Laws and Acts of Parliament of Scotland.

NASHE, T. (1904). Christ's Teares over Jerusalem. *In* Works of Thomas Nashe. London, Bullen. *2:* 172. (first ed. 1598).

NELSON, W. (1736). The Laws of England Concerning the Game. London. 3rd. ed. 71, 153.

NELSON, T. H., CLARKE, W. E. and BOYES, E. (1907). The Birds of Yorkshire. London, Brown. *2:* 284-90.

NEWSTEAD, R. (1894). The Heron and Heronries of Cheshire and North Wales. *Proc. Chester Soc. Nat. Sci. Lit. and Art. 4:* 234.

NICHOLSON, E. M. (1929). Report on the "British Birds" Census of Heronries, 1928. *Brit. Birds, 22:* 270-372.—(1930). Supplementary report on the "British Birds" Census of Heronries. *Brit. Birds, 23:* 324-337.—(1931). *Idem. Brit. Birds, 25:* 159-161.—(1935-38). An Index of Heron Population. *Brit. Birds, 28:* 332-41. *29:* 98-101. *30:* 202-05. *31:* 341-44. *32:* 138-44.

NIETHAMMER, G. (1938). Handbuch der Deutschen Vogelkunde. Leipzig, Akademische Verlagsgesellschaft M.B.H. Vol. 2, pp. 313-22.

NITZSCH, C. L. (1867). Pterylography. London, The Ray Society. English translation edited by P. L. Sclater. 127-29, Pl.

NORTH, M. E. W. (1931). Unrecorded Cambridgeshire Heronries. *Rep. Cambr. Bird Cl.*

NORTH, M. E. W. (1939). Field notes on certain Raptorials and Water-Birds in Kenya Colony. *Ibis*, (14), *3:* 487-507 (491).

NORTHUMBERLAND, HENRY ALGERNON PERCY, FIFTH EARL of. (1878). The Household Books of the Lord William Howard of Naworth Castle. Durham, London and Edinburgh, Surtees Society.

DEGLI ODDI. E. A. and MOLTONI, E. (1930). Osservazione fatte nelle Garzaie di Greggio (Vercelli) e di Casalino (Novara). *Riv. Sci. Nat. "Natura,"* *21:* 1-32.—(1933). Ulteriore Notizie sulle Garzaie di Greggio (Vercelli) e di Casalino (Novara). *Ibid. 72:* 91-135.

OLDERZ, C. (1936). Northerly breeding of Grey Heron, *Ardea cinerea. Fauna och Flora, Uppsala, Heft 6.*

OLIVER, W. R. B. (1930). New Zealand Birds. Wellington, N.Z., Fine Arts. 358.

ONSLOW, G. H. (1946). Ravens nesting in a Heronry. *Brit. Birds, 39:* 212.

OSBALDISTON, W. A. (1792). The British Sportsman. London, printed by J. Stead.

PARKER, E. (1942). Oddities of Natural History. London, Seeley Service. 107-108.

PARSONS, A. G. (1947). Herons Feeding by Probing under Water. *Brit. Birds, 40:* 313-14.

PATON, E. R. and PIKE, O. G. (1929). The Birds of Ayrshire. London, Witherby. 119-20.

PATTEN, C. J. (1906). The Aquatic Birds of Great Britain. London, Porter. 15.

PAYNE-GALLWEY, SIR R., BART. (1882). The Fowler in Ireland. London, Van Voorst. 244-47.

PENNANT, T. (1768). The British Zoology. 2nd ed. London, Benjamin White. 2: 355-56, 360. (first ed. 1766).

PERCY, LORD W. (1932). Lecture to British Ornithologist's Club on the use of the Powder-Down patches in the Bittern. Bull. Brit. Orn. Cl. 52: 136-38.

—(1932). On the use of Powder-Down patches in the Bittern. Country Life. 18 June. 00.—(1933). The Heron. Country Life, 1 July. 704-06, 15 July. 31-33.

PETERS, J. L. (1931). Check-List of the Birds of the World. Cambridge, Mass. Vol. 1.

PFLUGBEIL, A. and RINGLEBEN, H. (1938). Beringungsergebnisse bei brandens-burgischen Fischreihern, Ardea c. cinerea L. Berlin.

PICKERING, M. W. (1944). Herons swimming and diving. Brit. Birds, 38: 136.

PONTOPPIDAN, E. (1755). The Natural History of Norway. English ed. London. 2: 77.

POULTON, E. B. (1890). The Colours of Animals, Their Meaning and Use. London, Kegan Paul, Trench, Trubner & Co.

POWERSCOURT, THE VISCOUNT. (1945). Fishing in Eire. Irish Times 9 Nov.

PRESCHER, H. (1937). Wiederfunde in Pommern beringter Fischreirer. Sonder-bruck aus Dohrniana 16. Band, 1937.

PYCRAFT, W. P. (1908). The Powder-Down of the Heron. Brit. Birds, 1: 343-46.

RALFE, P. G. (1905). The Birds of the Isle of Man. Edinburgh, Douglas. 149-52.

RAMSAY, L. N. G. (1914). Bird-Life of the Anatolian Plateau (Asia Minor). Ibis, (10), 2: 368.

REINHARDT, J. (1861). On the Birds hitherto observed in Greenland. Ibis, (1), 3: 9-10.

RILEY, J. H. (1938). Birds of Siam and the Malay Peninsula in the U.S. National Museum. Washington, U.S. Govt. Printing Off.

RINTOUL, L. J. and BAXTER, E. V. (1928). The geographical distribution and status of birds in Scotland. Edinburgh, Oliver & Boyd.

RINTOUL, L. J. and BAXTER, E. V. (1935). A vertebrate fauna of Forth. Edinburgh, Oliver & Boyd.

RITCHIE, J. (1932). Systematic "Beating" by Herons. Brit. Birds, 25: 228.

ROBERTS, A. (1940). The Birds of South Africa. London, Witherby.

ROBINSON, H. C. and CHASEN, F. N. (1936). The Birds of the Malay Peninsula. London, Witherby. Vol. 3.

ROLLAND, E. (1879). Faune Populaire de la France.

RUTTLEDGE, R. F. (1949). Bill and Leg Colouration of the Common Heron in the Breeding Season. Brit. Birds, 42: 42-45.

RYVES, B. H. (1948). Bird Life in Cornwall. London. Collins.

SAGER, H. (1940). Beringungsergebnisse an schleswig-holsteinischen Fischreihern. Z. Jagdk. 11, Heft 3/4. Berlin.

ST. JOHN, C. (1849). Wild Sports and Natural History of the Highlands.

London, Murray. pp. 28-29. (first ed. 1846).—(1849). A Tour in Sutherland. London, Murray. *1:* 215.

de SAINTE-PALAYE, M. la CURNE. The Vows of the Heron. In Thomas Wright's Political Poems and Songs (1859) temp. Edw. *III*—Ric. *III.* London, Longman. *1:* 1-25.

SALTER, J. H. (1904). Ornithological notes from Mid-Wales. Zoologist, (4), *8:* 66-71 (p. 70-71).

SALVIN, F. H. and BRODERICK, F. W. (1873). Falconry in the British Isles. London, Van Voorst. 2nd ed. 80-81.

SCHAANNING, H. T. L. (1923). Om endel nye fugler for Spitsbergen-omradet. *Norsk. Orn. Tidsskr. 4:* 221.—(1937). Fortsatte Resultater (6) fra den Internasjonale Ringmerkning vedrorende Norske. *Stavanger Mus. Arshefte, 1935-36:* 89-102.

SCHARFF, USSHER, COLE, NEWTON, DIXON and WESTROPP. (1906). Exploration of Caves, Co. Clare. *Proc. R. Irish. Acad.* 33(B): 1.

SCHLEGEL, H. and WÜLVERHORST, A. H. V. VAN. (1844-53). Traité de Fauconnerie. Leyden & Dusseldorf.

SCHÜZ, E. and WEIGOLD, H. (1931). Atlas des Vogelzugs nach den Beringungsergebnissen bei palaearktischen vogeln. Berlin, Friedlander.

SCHÜZ, E. (1943). Uber die Jungenaufzucht des Weissen Storches (*C. ciconia*) *Z̧. Morph. Ökol. Tiere, 40:* 181-237.

SCLATER, P. L. (1889). On animals noted in the Zoological Gardens at Rotterdam. *Proc. Z̧ool. Soc. 1889:* 219-20.

SEIGNE, J. W. (1930). A Bird Watcher's Note Book. London, Allan. 110-11.

SHARPE, R. B. (1898). Catalogue of the Birds in the British Museum. London, Trustees Brit. Mus. *26:* 66-85, 268-69.

SLATER, H. H. (1901). Manual of the Birds of Iceland. Edinburgh, Douglas. 38-39.

SOUTHERN, H. N. (1932). Close-ups of Birds. London, Hutchinson. 49-50, 52.

SPALLANZANI, L. (1789). Dissertations relative to the Natural History of Animals and Vegetables. English translation of the Modena ed. *1:* 103-18 (Dissertation 2).

STANFORD, J. K. and TICEHURST, C. B. (1935). Notes on some new and rarely recorded Burmese Birds. *Ibis*, (13), *5:* 249-279 (277).

STANLEY, E. (1851). A Familiar History of Birds. London, Parker, pp. 339-40 (first ed. 1835).

STAPLES, C. P. and HARRISON, J. G. (1949). Further as to colour change without a moult, etc. *Bull. Brit. Orn. Cl. 69:* 10.

STEVENSON, H. (1866). Birds of Norfolk. London, Van Voorst. *2:* 131-32.

SWAINSON, C. (1885). Provincial Names and Folk Lore of British Birds. London. English Dialect Soc. 144-45.

SWAN, J. (1635). Speculum Mundi, or the Glasse Representing the Face of the World. 400.

SWANN, H. K. (1913). A Dictionary of English and Folk-Names of British Birds. London, Witherby. 121-22, 264.

TAIT, W. C. (1934). The Birds of Portugal. London, Witherby.

TAKA TSUKASA, PRINCE N. (1941). Japanese Birds. Board of Tourist Industry Jap. Govt. Railways.

TAYLOR, J. SNEYD. (1937). Notes from the Graaff-Reinet. *Ostrich, 8:* 31. — (1938). Birds observed at the Van Ryneveld's Pass Irrigation Lake, Graaff-Reinet. *Ostrich. 9:* 22.

TEIGNMOUTH, LORD. (1878). Reminiscences of Many Years. Edinburgh, Douglas. *1:* 305.

THAYER, G. H. (1909). Concealing-Colouration in the Animal Kingdom. New York, Macmillan. 58, 85.

THORPE, W. H., COTTON, P. T. and HOLMES, P.F. (1936). Notes on the birds of Lakes Ochrid, Malik and Prespa and adjacent parts of Yugoslavia, Albania and Greece. *Ibis,* (13), 6: 557-80 (572).

TICEHURST, C. B. (1910). On the Food of the Common Heron. *Brit. Birds, 4:* 85-86.—(1923). The Birds of Sind. *Ibis,* (11), *5:* 266-67.

TICEHURST, C. B. and WHISTLER, H. (1929). A Spring tour through Yugoslavia. *Ibis,* (12), *5:* 655-89 (685).—(1932). On the Ornithology of Albania. *Ibis,* (13), *2:* 40-93 (80).

TICEHURST, N. F. (1907). On the Nesting of a Pair of Herons on Dungeness Beach. *Brit. Birds, 1:* 97-101.—(1938). The Migratory Status of the Heron in Great Britain. *Brit. Birds, 32:* 242-46.

TUCKER, B. W. (1930). The Heron in Somerset. *Proc. Som. Arch. Nat. Hist. Soc. 76:* 31-52.—(1946). Bill-Colour of Heron in Breeding-Season. *Brit. Birds, 39:* 128.—(1949). Remarks on a seasonal colour change in the bill and legs of herons. *Brit. Birds, 42:* 46-50.

TUCKER, B. W. and OORDT, G. T. VAN. (1929). Further notes on the ornithology of the Naples district. *Ibis,* (12), *5:* 499-523 (519).

TURNER, W. (1903). De Historia Avium. A. H. Evans' ed. Cambridge, University Press. 39. (first ed. 1544).

USSHER, J. R. and WARREN, R. (1900). Birds of Ireland. London, Gurney & Jackson. 159-60.

VAUGHAN, R. E. & JONES, K. H. (1913). On the Birds of South-Eastern China. *Ibis,* (10), *1:* 368.

VERWEY, J. (1930). Die Paarungsbiologie des Fischreihers. *Zool. Jahrb. Jena. Zool. Physiol. 48:* 1-120.

VINCENT, A. W. (1945). On the Breeding Habits of some African Birds. *Ibis, 87:* 82.

VÖLKER, O. (1936). Yellow Feather-Pigment of Wellensittich—*Melopsittacus undulatus* Shaw. *J. Orn. 84:* 618-30.

WALTON, ISAAC. (1909). The Compleat Angler. London, Cassell. 151. (first ed. 1653).

WARREN, R. (1910). Herons Breeding Twice in the Season. *Zoologist,* (4), *14:* 341.

WATT, H. B. (1908). List of Scottish Heronries. *Ann. Scot. Nat. Hist. 1908 65;* 218-23.

WATTERS, J. J. (1853). The Natural History of the Birds of Ireland. Dublin, McGlashan. 131.

WHISTLER, H. (1936). Further observations from Albania. *Ibis*, (13), *6:* 335-56 (349).

WHITAKER, J. I. S. (1905). The Birds of Tunisia. London, Porter. 162-63.—(1899). Abnormal nest of *Ardea cinerea. Bull. Brit. Orn. Cl. 8:* 37.

WHITE, GILBERT. (1924). Natural History of Selborne. Letter 22. R. Kearton's Ed. (first ed. 1788).

WILLIAMS, A. (1881). Ornithological notes from Dublin. *Zoologist,* (3), *5:* 468.

WILLIAMSON, J. (1740). The British Angler, London..

WILLIAMSON, K. (1947). Notes on the occurrences and habits of some Passage-Migrants and rare vagrants in the Faroe Islands. *Ibis, 89:* 111.—(1947). The Atlantic Islands. London, Collins. 84.

WILSON, J. O. (1933). Birds of Westmorland and the Northern Pennines. London, Hutchinson. 221.

WITHERBY, H. F. (1909). Recovery of Marked Birds. *Brit. Birds, 3:* 219, and subsequent annual reports to 1936.—(1928). On the Birds of Central Spain. *Ibis,* (12), *4:* 587-663 (652).

WITHERBY, H. F., JOURDAIN, F. C. R., TICEHURST, N. F. and TUCKER, B. W. (1939). The Handbook of British Birds. London, Witherby. *3:* 111-12, 125, 156, 162-63.

WRIGLEY, J. (1892). Notes on the Bird Life of Formby. Liverpool.

YARRELL, W. (1871-85). A History of British Birds. *4:* 162-63.

ZEUNER, F. E. (1946). Dating the Past. London. Methuen. 108.

ZITKOV, B. M. and BUTURLIN, S. A. (1906). Beitrage zur Ornithofauna des Gouv. Simbirsk. 202-204.

ADDENDA

BAKER, E. C. S. (1930). The Fauna of British India. 2nd. Ed., 8 : 560. London, Taylor & Francis.

HUTSON, H. P. W. & BANNERMAN, D. A. (1930). The Birds of Northern Nigeria. *Ibis,* (12), 6 : 600-38 (611).

STRIJBOS, J. P. (1935). De Blauwe Reiger, Amsterdam.

INDEX

Special Volumes

THE BADGER   ERNEST NEAL

THE REDSTART   JOHN BUXTON

THE YELLOW WAGTAIL   STUART SMITH

THE GREENSHANK   DESMOND NETHERSOLE-THOMPSON

THE FULMAR   JAMES FISHER

FLEAS, FLUKES AND CUCKOOS   MIRIAM ROTHSCHILD & THERESA CLAY

THE HERRING GULL'S WORLD   NIKO TINBERGEN

MUMPS, MEASLES AND MOSAICS   KENNETH M. SMITH & ROY MARKHAM

THE NEW NATURALIST LIBRARY

"What must impress the readers of the volumes is that they are at once books for the expert and the general reader, a combination not easy to achieve." GLASGOW HERALD